Foundations for the Daily Maths Lesson

Dawn Lyell

Contents

Published by Step Forward Publishing Limited
The Coach House, Cross Road, Leamington Spa CV32 5PB   Tel: 01926 420046
© Step Forward Publishing Limited 2002
Foundations for the Daily Maths Lesson   ISBN: 1-902438-61-2

Introduction

The Government launched the National Numeracy Strategy as part of its drive to raise standards in mathematics. Since September 1999, schools have been required to provide a structured daily mathematics lesson for pupils of primary age. Oral and mental work feature strongly in each lesson and teachers teach the whole class together for much of the time.

In September 2000, the Foundation Stage of education was extended to include the Reception year. Children in Reception classes now work towards the Early Learning Goals as well as the numeracy Framework – and Reception teachers have two documents to take into account when planning mathematics instead of one.

However, the Early Learning Goals for Mathematical Development were amended to take account of the *National Numeracy Strategy*, and the *Curriculum Guidance for the Foundation Stage* is also clear that 'Reception teachers may choose to cover the elements of the literacy hour and daily mathematics lesson across the day rather than in a single unit of time'. The *Framework for Teaching Mathematics from Reception to Year 6* emphasises that 'your aim should be to prepare children, by the end of Reception, for the dedicated mathematics lesson', so helping them to make a smooth transition to Year 1.

The Early Learning Goals match the key objectives of the numeracy Framework and therefore each document contains valuable information on progression that should be referred to. Your judgement is crucial and flexibility is important. Children bring with them a variety of experiences. Your aim should be to build upon a child's previous experience and knowledge and make their future experiences meaningful.

The daily mathematics lesson

The daily maths lesson consists of three elements:

- The oral/mental starter
- Main teaching activity
- Plenary

When children start in Reception, they may not have the concentration levels, or the social skills, to work as part of a large group. Numeracy sessions should, therefore, consist initially of three separate components, consolidated into one daily maths lesson by the end of the year. By the summer term, all children should be taking part in a single session lasting no more than 45 minutes in preparation for Year 1.

The oral/mental starter

When children begin Reception, sitting in large groups for about ten minutes is probably as much as you can expect. This time is ideal for rhymes, action songs and counting activities. By doing this in large groups, all children gain confidence by working together and developing a 'can do' culture. The oral/mental starter provides reinforcement of mathematical vocabulary and counting, as well as key number skills and concepts.

The main teaching activity

The main teaching activity includes some whole-class instruction, then group activities can be spread throughout the day, if you wish. Activities should be at three levels: adult-led, adult-supported where the adult provides support as an expert play partner, and child-initiated.

During the main teaching activity you can introduce a new topic to the children. You can model or demonstrate skills to introduce new concepts, extend the understanding of a mathematical concept, revisit and consolidate knowledge. This is a good time to assess a child's understanding of a concept.

As children progress, they should need less adult support. Independence needs to be developed and managed. Independent activities should be short. It is best that there is a visible outcome so that you can assess the completed task.

Activities that are directed or supported by adults can later become child-led activities.

The National Numeracy Strategy suggests two models for the main teaching activity:

- Introduce topic to the whole class
- Several activities planned for the day/week (differentiated)
- Follow whole-class activity with practical activity (teacher supported)
- Group work with a teaching assistant
- Later another group can work with the teacher
- Other children can be involved in free/structured activities
- During the course of the week all children will be involved in mathematical activities supported by a teacher or teaching assistant

- Introduce topic to whole class/large group
- Plan several activities to follow (differentiated)
- Teacher works with group
- Assistant works with group as expert 'play partner'
- Group can do short independent activity/structured play
- Aim for all of these activities to end at a similar time for plenary

The latter model is probably most suited to the summer term in Reception, depending on the availability of support.

The plenary

The plenary takes place at the end of a session, for example before lunch or home time, and can consist of consolidating rhymes, emphasising key teaching points and building on the day's activities – it is not just a 'show and tell' exercise.

'Numeracy is a proficiency which involves confidence and competence with numbers and measures. It requires an understanding of the number system, a repertoire of computational skills and an inclination and ability to solve number problems in a variety of contexts.'

Framework for Teaching Mathematics from Reception to Year 6

Planning

You can promote, reinforce and supplement the use of mathematical concepts and vocabulary by planning activities across the curriculum (that is, outside the allocated maths session). Through the use of stories and rhymes, PE and music a variety of skills can be developed related to numeracy, for example counting jumps, claps, reciting numbers in order – 'One, two, three, four, five, Once I caught a fish alive', counting in twos – 'Two, four, six, eight, Mary at the cottage gate', retelling stories and sequencing events.

- By pretending to be robots and following instructions in order to retrieve an object, children have the opportunity to use positional vocabulary in a meaningful context.

- Art/graphic areas, sand and water play can all support and reinforce the theme of the numeracy session. They can also allow subjects previously covered to be revisited.

- The use of information technology is important. Young children enjoy listening to tapes of number rhymes, especially when accompanied by illustrations and books.

- A language master, with simple instructions – 'Draw three flowers', 'Draw four trees', 'Draw a tall tree' – can be used for children to work independently.

- Roamers can be given covers and decorated to create a character, such as a ladybird, and then children program the Roamer to reach a leaf, for example.

- Television programmes and videos often have characters which appeal to the children and there is computer software designed specifically to develop mathematical concepts.

About this book

This book is structured along similar lines to the medium-term sample plans provided by the National Numeracy Strategy. Each term is divided into 12 units with the sixth and twelfth unit devoted to assessment. Most units consist of five sessions which encompass approximately one week's work. The medium-term plans state that the number of teaching days for each unit can be determined once the children have settled into school. You may wish to change the position of the unit 'Shape, space and measures'. This is not a problem. Just remember that the mental/oral starters need to remain in the original order. The assessment units should not take a full week, so use the remaining sessions to revisit any areas that need reinforcement.

A variety of activities are suggested for each day of the week. The objectives for each unit – or week – are listed in the left-hand column, along with key/words or phrases for use during the week.

The children should be made aware of these objectives or targets and they should be displayed. For example: 'This week we are going to count up to five objects'; 'This week we are going to count to ten in ones'.

The vocabulary given for each unit is based on the DfEE published list for Reception (*Mathematical Vocabulary*). It is important that any new vocabulary introduced is used consistently by all adults. Key words on flash cards can be shown to the children and act as prompts when teaching. These words can be displayed around the classroom as part of a numeracy display.

Each day or session is broken down into four main sections:

- The oral/mental starter
- The main teaching activity
- Group activities
- The plenary

An oral/mental starter is provided, but you may have your own personal favourite rhymes/songs for counting that you can use instead.

The main teaching activity usually consists of a short session whereby a large group of children are introduced to the main theme of the lesson before the three activities take place. (Do not feel that all three activities need to be done simultaneously – organise your class to suit your own circumstances.)

The three group activities usually correspond to the following approaches:

1) Teacher-initiated and directed

2) With adult support

3) Child-initiated/independent

The plenary can pull together elements of the numeracy session and also other related activities that reinforce the objective.

At the end of this book, various photocopiable resources are provided to support some of the activities suggested. These are not worksheets. You can enlarge some of them for use in class/large group demonstrations. It is worth laminating or covering them to prolong their classroom life. Some of the resources could be sent home for parents to use.

The role of additional adults

There can be a variety of support staff working within the Reception area, for example EMAG (Ethnic Minority Achievement Grant) teachers, teaching assistants and special needs support. Wherever possible all these staff need to be involved in planning and must be aware of the teaching objectives. The strategies and vocabulary used need to be consistent. Make sure that everyone is clear about the group and the children they will be working with. In the oral/mental starter session, the adult should have a specific role, in other words, sitting with the children, encouraging the less confident, translating instructions or specific vocabulary or observing children to record responses. At the end of a session, the additional adult can support children in the plenary as in the beginning. During the main activities, any observations need to be discussed and used to aid future planning.

Home/school partnerships

It is important that parents are partners in their child's education. Parents need to be informed about the targets/objectives that their child will be working towards during Reception. By holding parents' workshops and courses and inviting them into school, you can inform them about and involve them in the strategies used in numeracy. Encourage children to bring things from home that can be incorporated into displays and discussions. Simple games can be sent home, too. It is also useful for parents to find out what happens in Year 1 to enable them to see progression.

Assessment

By the end of the Foundation Stage, most children will have achieved the Early Learning Goals for Mathematical Development. These goals can be used as assessment criteria. Assessment is an intrinsic part of future planning. After an initial assessment, establish the next step to support and extend the child's mathematical experiences. The Numeracy Strategy builds in time for assessment at the end of each half term (Units 6 and 12). However, it is important that informal assessment is ongoing. Each person who works with and alongside the child should have some input into this to ensure an accurate overall picture. Specific assessments can be built into the weekly plan, for example reciting numbers one to ten.

An assessment sheet is included in this book (page 6) which uses the key objectives from the numeracy Framework. Space is provided to list six names and write a brief comment.

Further guidance, *Using Assess and Review Lessons* (Ref DfES 0632/2001) has been published on assessing and reviewing children's progress in numeracy. Pages 13 to 15 contain examples of questions that can be used to assess a child's understanding against the key objectives.

'Mathematical understanding should be developed through stories, songs, games and imaginative play, so that children enjoy using and experimenting with numbers.'

Curriculum Guidance for the Foundation Stage

Classroom essentials

Every Reception class needs an area where numeracy resources can be displayed and are accessible. The following are basic essential items:

■ Large 100 square/large number line/ individual number lines

■ Numeral cards (zero to 20) for each child (enlarged cards for whole class activities)

■ Dot cards (zero to ten) for each child (enlarged cards for whole class activities)

■ Washing line to display numeral/dot cards

■ Cubes, for example Unifix/Multilink

■ Counting objects, for example beads, bears, cubes, counters, buttons

■ Sorting trays

■ Dominoes

■ Dice, including blank dice (to label in various ways)

■ Blank grids (2 x 3, 3 x 3, 2 x 5)for various games, eg bingo

■ Target board

■ Coins (real, plastic and large facsimile)

■ Access to computer/Roamer/tape recorder

■ 2-d/3-d shapes

■ Feely bag or box

Note: Dot cards, numeral cards, coins, a number line and tracks are provided as photocopiable resources at the back of this book.

ASSESSMENT

Key objectives for Reception Child's name							
Say and use the number names in order in familiar contexts							
Count reliably up to 10 everyday objects							
Recognise numerals 1-9							
Use language such as more/less, greater/smaller, heavier/lighter, to compare two numbers or quantities							
In practical activities and discussion, begin to use the vocabulary involved in adding and subtracting							
Find one more or one less than a number from 1-10							
Begin to relate addition to combining two groups of objects, and subtraction to taking away							
Talk about, recognise and recreate simple patterns							
Use language such as circle or bigger to describe the shape and size of solids and flat shapes							
Use everyday words to describe position							
Use developing mathematical ideas and methods to solve practical problems							

Note: Enlarge to A3

Counting

Unit 1

Objectives:

Say and use number names up to five in order in familiar contexts, such as rhymes, songs, stories and counting games

Recite number names in order from one to five (progressing to ten)

Vocabulary:

count, count up to, count in ones, counting

number, one, two, three, four, five, six, seven, eight, nine, ten

How many?, show me, match, sort, count all

References:

National Numeracy Strategy pages 2-8

Curriculum Guidance for the Foundation Stage pages 68, 74, 75

Session 1:

Resources:
Objects to count - cubes, counters, buttons, beads
Box or bag for counting objects out of
Farm/zoo animals (two of each) or pairs of socks/mittens
Paper and crayons (for drawing)

Starter

Sing 'Two little dicky birds', using actions. Invite the children to join in. Ask them how many birds were sitting on the wall. Sing it again and this time encourage everyone to join in. Ask them to make sure that they all have two little birds. Count them. Sing the song once more.

Main teaching activity

Explain that this week they are going to be learning how to count up to five. To do this, they need to remember the numbers in the right order. Ask them to help you draw a picture of yourself. Begin by drawing a large circle on the board. Say: 'This is my face. What shall I draw next? Eyes. How many have I got?' Point to them and count. Draw one eye and pause. 'Is that right?' No. Draw another and count. 'How many eyes have I drawn?' Two. Repeat and add other features. (You can extend the activity by drawing a body, with arms and legs.)

Group activities

1   Provide a box (or bag) containing a variety of objects for counting. Restrict the variety to avoid confusion. Explain that you want them to sort and count the objects in the box. (Sorting and how to sort needs to be modelled before it can be used as an independent activity.) Children take turns in removing an object from the box and identifying it, for example a cube. The next child takes another object. It's another cube. Ask: 'How many cubes are there? Let's count them'. (Touch and move the objects as they are counted.) When the box is empty, ask the children to count how many cubes/beads/bears there are.

2   Provide the children with a selection of farm/zoo animals (two of each variety) or you might want to use pairs of socks/mittens instead. Children match them into groups of two (pairs).

3   Let children draw pictures of themselves. (You could provide an outline of a face for them to add the facial features.)

Plenary

Discuss the pictures the children drew of themselves (activity 3). Count eyes, ears, nose, and so on. (Some children may have attempted to draw hands. Count how many fingers they have drawn and ask 'How many do you have?') Look at the farm/zoo animals (activity 2). Get children to count how many sheep/lions there are. Touch and move each animal as it is counted.

Session 2:

Resources:
Toy bears with corresponding number of cups and plates
Two sets of dot cards (one to five) (photocopiable sheet 1)
Cubes for towers
Selection of cubes/counters and sorting trays or margarine tubs (labelled with one to five dots)
Old magazines for cutting out pictures
Cutting and sticking materials
Materials to make a large class counting book

Starter
Sing 'One, two, three, four, five, once I caught a fish alive'.

Main teaching activity
Explain that today they are going to count to five, using their fingers to help them. Start with a closed fist, and then straighten one digit at a time as the number is said. Repeat. Say: 'Let's count to three. Everybody show me three fingers'. Ask a child to get three cubes. Count them. Make the three cubes into a tower. 'How many cubes are there?' Using three bears, let the children give each bear a cup and a plate. Count how many bears. 'How many plates?' Make sure that each item is touched as it is counted. Show the children the cards with dots on them (one dot, two dots and three dots) and count the dots.

Group activities
1   You will need two sets of dot cards (one to three at first) and a selection of cubes. Place the dot cards face down. Explain that you are going to take turns to turn over a card and count the dots (you'll need to model the activity first). Then take the same amount of cubes, counting them as they are removed from the centre of the table. Make them into a tower. The winner of the game is the child who collects a tower of one, two and three cubes. (If a child turns over a card that would mean duplicating a tower they miss that turn.)

2   Use a selection of cubes/counters and sorting trays. Label sections of the trays with varying amounts of dots (one to five). (Use dots as children can count and match the objects.) Ask children to put the correct amount of cubes/counters in the trays.

3   Children can cut and stick pictures, draw or print sets of objects to make a large class counting book. (Children may wish to draw items for the bears.)

Plenary
Discuss activities 2 and 3. It is important that the objects/items are counted. Show a card that has four dots on. Count all the dots: one, two, three, four. Count up to four with fingers. Ask the children to remember this for tomorrow.

Session 3:

Resources:
Tinder Box (A & C Black)
Large outline of house (for wall display)
Pictures cut from catalogues showing features of a house/garden – chimneys, doors, windows, trees and flowers
Selection of cubes/counters and sorting trays labelled with one to five dots (as for session 2)
Materials for large class counting book (as for session 2)

Starter
Begin by singing 'How many people live in your house?' from *Tinder Box*. Use fingers to count: one, my mummy; two, my daddy; three, my sister; four, my brother. 'There's one more. Who could it be?' The children hold up five fingers when they say 'ME!'

Main teaching activity
Count from one to five using fingers. Choose four children to stand up. Everyone counts them together. Change the amount of children standing up. Count this group.

Group activities
1   Show the children the outline of the house. You might want to use pictures created by the children for additional counting opportunities. Explain that the house needs two chimneys on the roof. Ask a child to pick the appropriate pictures. Count them and then stick them to the picture. 'Can you find me four windows?' Repeat using different amounts for doors, clouds, trees, flowers and so on.

2   As for session 2 but extend to using four dots.

3   As for session 2 but extend to using five items.

Plenary
Children respond to questions based upon the wall display. 'How many windows are there?' 'What can you see in the picture?' Encourage the children to say 'I can see four windows, five flowers', and so on.

Session 4:

Resources:
Set of dot cards (photocopiable sheets 1 and 2)

Washing line and pegs

Dominoes

Counters/cubes

Items to bury in the sand tray (shells, coins, buttons)

Starter
Sing 'One, two, three, four, five, once I caught a fish alive'. Count from one to five.

Main teaching activity
Using dot cards one to five, count the dots on each card. Put the cards on the floor in random order. Count from one to five. Ask: 'When we count, what number do we start with?' One. Ask a child to get the card with one dot on. Peg the card to the left on the washing line. 'What number do we say next?' Point to the washing line and say 'one', prompting the children to continue with 'two'. Ask another child to pick up the card with two dots on it and peg it to the line. Continue until all five cards are on the line. Count from one to five, pointing at the cards.

Group activities
1   Play dominoes. Put a selection of dominoes in the middle of the table. You pick the first domino (showing one and two). Ask: 'How many spots are at this end?' Count two. A child then finds another domino with two dots at one end and matches them together. (Make sure you choose dominoes to suit the ability of each group. If children lack confidence, you could perhaps use two sets with just one, two and three dots.)

2   Using dot cards. Children put them in the correct order (they can use the washing line as a point of reference) then make towers or collections of counters, corresponding to the dots.

3   Bury items in the sand tray. Children have to find five items, for example five shells, five bears, five buttons.

Plenary
Discuss activity 2. Count together the number of items in their collections.

How many items did they find in the sand?

Can the children begin to explain how to play dominoes? The skill of explaining needs to be developed and will need considerable scaffolding by the use of visual and verbal prompts: 'What did I do?' 'Then what did you do?' 'How did you do that?' 'Why did you do that?' If the children become accustomed to hearing these questions they will begin to use them in play/independent situations.

Session 5:

Resources:
Cubes

Set of dot cards (photocopiable sheets 1 and 2)

Dominoes

Paper (for each child), crayons, paints and pens to make posters

Starter
Sing 'One man went to mow'.

Main teaching activity
Refer to the wall display. Ask how many doors they can see on the house. 'How many chimneys can you see? Let's count them.'

Count up to five together using your fingers then explain that you're now going to play a game called 'Show me'. When you say a number you want them to hold up the same number of fingers. 'Show me one': the children hold up one finger. 'Show me three': the children hold up three fingers. Check by counting out loud together: 'One, two, three'.

Group activities
1   Put some cubes and the dot cards in the middle of the group. Ask a child to get the card that has three dots. Now you need three cubes. Ask another child to get three cubes. Move the cubes as the number is said (this reinforces the idea that the last number said is the amount). When towers one to five have been made, arrange them in a staircase pattern. Let the children make their own staircase and encourage them to keep recounting. Say a number. The children have to hold up the corresponding tower. (To challenge some children, don't say the number, just hold up a dot card or fingers briefly. This develops the ability to recognise pattern.)

2   Play dominoes.

3   Give children a sheet of paper to make a counting poster. They can draw or stick objects onto the paper.

Plenary
Show the children the counting book that they made earlier in the week. Discuss the way the pages have been ordered.

Look at a number frieze. Count to ten. Point out that their posters and book only go up to five. Explain that you are going to make some more pages next lesson. Sing 'One, two, three, four, five'.

Counting

Unit 2

Objectives:

Say and use number names up to ten in order in familiar contexts, such as rhymes, songs and stories

Recite number names in order from one to ten

Count reliably up to five objects

Vocabulary:

count, count up to, count back from, start at, find, point to, show me, next, check, How many?

number, one, two, three, four, five, six, seven, eight, nine, ten

References:

National Numeracy Strategy pages 2-8

Curriculum Guidance for the Foundation Stage pages 68, 74, 75

Note: During this week children should have the opportunity to listen to number rhymes on tape.

Session 1:

Resources:

Large box/bag containing objects for counting (animals, beads, pasta shapes)

Sets of dot cards (photocopiable sheets 1 and 2)

Sorting trays or tubs (labelled with different numbers of spots, some labelled with colours)

A die and counters

Sand tray

Starter

Recite 'One, two, buckle my shoe'. Encourage the children to join in the actions. Count from one to ten using fingers, making sure that the fingers are straightened as a number is said.

Main teaching activity

Tell the children that you have a box with lots of things in but they are all muddled up. Take each item out of the box. Count each item as it is removed. Ask, for example, 'How many books are there? Let's count them'. Children then match objects to dot cards. You can show them the corresponding numeral - exposure to numerals is important but should not be emphasised too early as counting skills are paramount.

Group activities

1   Prepare some dot cards - enough for one set per child in the group (shuffled). The children take turns to take a card. The aim is to collect a complete set of cards (representing one to ten). Children then order them. Ask: 'What card do we start with?' 'What will come next?' (Increase/decrease the amount of cards used depending on the children's concentration span.)

2   Use sorting trays labelled with one to five spots. Children roll a die and count the spots, then put the corresponding amount of counters into the trays.

3   Label tubs with colours. Bury coloured counters in the sand tray. Children find the counters and put them in the corresponding tubs.

Plenary

Using the tubs from activity 3, ask various questions, for example 'How many red counters did you find? Let's count them'. Arrange them in a different pattern to that shown on the dot card. Ask a child to find the dot card. Move the counters onto the dot card (to show that the count doesn't change with position).

Session 2:

Resources:

Cubes – five per child of the same colour

Sets of dot cards (photocopiable sheets 1 and 2) - one set per child in group 1

Sorting trays labelled with one to six spots

A die and counters

Materials for class number book

Cubes and a die (for plenary)

Starter

Count from one to ten. Use fingers to count from one to ten. Play 'Show me' as in Unit 1, session 5.

Main teaching activity

Children sit in a horse-shoe shape. Give each child five cubes of the same colour. (I find it useful to make sure that one child has red, the next blue, the next green, and so on - it prevents children confusing their cubes with another child's.) Ask the children to count how many cubes they have. Then explain that you want them to count two cubes and make them into a tower. Say 'Show me your tower of two'. Children hold up their tower. Ask them to put their cubes back. Say 'This time I want you to get four cubes and make them into a tower. When I say "Show me your tower" I want you to hold up your tower'. This activity will be used as a starter activity called 'Towers'. Now take six cubes and count them, touching and moving each one as it is counted. Everyone joins in the recount. Make a tower, counting each cube. Ask 'How many have I got in my tower?'

Group activities

1   As for session 1 but extend to six.

2   As for session 1 but extend to six.

3   Children continue making the class number book, by cutting or painting pictures for the number six.

Plenary

Sing 'One man went to mow' up to six men. Ask a child to get six cubes. Count them. Take a die. Children take turns in rolling the die, then jumping or clapping the number of times shown on the die.

Session 3:

Resources:

Large laminated ladybird (photocopiable sheet 8)

Ten spots (for ladybird) and Blu-Tack (for sticking on spots)

Ladybird cards (photocopiable sheet 9)

Cubes, such as Unifix (made into towers)

Sorting trays/tubs labelled with spots

Ladybird outlines for children (photocopiable sheet 8)

Paint/rubber stamps

Leaf shapes cut from green paper

Starter

Sing 'Six little ducks went swimming one day' (adapted from 'Five little ducks …'). Ask 'How many ducks did we start with?' Six. 'Show me six fingers.' Explain that now you are going to count forward to six and then back from six to one. Remind them to straighten their fingers as they count up and fold them down as they count back.

Main teaching activity

Make a large laminated ladybird (using the outline on photocopiable sheet 8). Begin to stick on the ladybird spots one at a time (with the Blu-Tack), counting aloud as each one is placed. When you get to six spots, ask the children to predict what number will be next. Put one more spot on. Say that now you're going to count them all to see if they are correct. All count together. 'How many are there?' 'Yes, there are seven.' Repeat until there are ten spots on the ladybird.

Group activities

1   Play ladybird Pelmanism (pairs) using the ladybird cards on photocopiable sheet 9. Spread two sets (20) of cards face down. Children take turns to turn over two cards and see if they are the same. Ask the children to count the spots on each ladybird and tell the group how many spots each card shows. Encourage the children to watch carefully and try to remember the cards' positions so they can make a pair when it is their turn. (Depending on the group, you may wish to use cards with a value up to five.)

2   Use a collection of cubes already made into towers. Children sort the towers by counting the cubes in each tower and putting them in the labelled tubs. You may wish to put a selection of towers into a bag for each child. Put a tub labelled, for example, with seven spots but do not have any towers of seven. The children can attempt to make a tower using loose cubes to go into the tub. (Extend to seven or reduce to three, depending on the group.)

3   Children add spots to blank ladybird outlines using paint or rubber stamps.

Plenary

Put green paper leaf shapes on the floor. Count the number of spots on a ladybird (from activity 3). Put it on one leaf. Count the spots on another ladybird. Place that one on another leaf. Repeat. If more than one ladybird has the same number of spots, put them on the same leaf. You might want to label the leaves with dot cards and/or numeral cards.

See if there are any towers in the pot from activity 2. Count the number of spots on the pot (seven) and check the number of cubes in the towers the children have made.

Session 4:

Resources:

Ladybird cards, one for each child (photocopiable sheet 9)

Two sets of ladybird cards (for activity 1)

Selection of ladybird cards (for activity 2)

Pot of counters

Ladybird outlines, one for each child (photocopiable sheet 8)

Paint/rubber stamps

Large laminated ladybird (photocopiable sheet 9)

Starter

Count from one to ten. Sing 'Ten green bottles'. Hold up ten fingers; fold one down each time a bottle falls.

Main teaching activity

Give each child a ladybird card. Ask the children in turn to count how many spots there are on their ladybird. Ask the children to hold up their card if their ladybird has four spots. 'If your ladybird has two spots, show me!' 'If your ladybird has three spots, stand up!' Vary the response required from the children to keep up the momentum of the activity and sustain interest – make it fun!

Group activities

1   As for session 3.

2   Put a selection of ladybird cards and a pot of counters on the table. Children count the number of spots on a ladybird and count out the corresponding amount of counters. (If you want, you can provide a ladybird outline.) Children can check if they are correct by placing the counters on the ladybird's spots.

3   As for session 3.

Plenary

Place spots randomly on the large laminated ladybird. Ask the children for help in counting the spots. Where do they think you should start? Count them. Ask a child to get that number of counters (as in activity 2). Arrange them in a different pattern. Ask the child to recount. Choose a different place to begin the count. Do they think the amount will change if you start counting from a different place?

Session 5:

Resources:

Box of objects for counting (from session 1)

Collection of objects to count (animals, beads, pasta shapes)

Ladybird cards and counters

Beads and string (to make necklaces)

Drawing materials for class number book

Starter

Sing or read 'Ten in the bed' (a related resource is provided for Unit 5 – see photocopiable sheet 15). Count from one to ten and back.

Main teaching activity

Children sit in a horse-shoe shape. Ask everyone if they can remember your box with lots of things in it that were all muddled up. Explain that you want them to help you sort and count all the objects. Take them out one at a time, grouping items together, in other words putting all the crayons together, all the building bricks, all the counters. How many pencils are there? Ask a child to count them, touching each one as it is counted. How many are there?

Group activities

1   Using a collection of objects (sorting animals, beads, pasta shapes), ask children to count out a given number of objects. You can extend the quantity up to ten. However, it is important that the children can count a smaller number of objects reliably first. Make sure that the children touch and say one number for each object.

2   As for session 4.

3   Make necklaces using eight, nine or ten beads.

Plenary

Sing 'One, two, buckle my shoe'.

Show the children the class number book. Discuss any numbers up to ten that don't have a page. Explain that you want to finish the book. You still need a page for numbers nine and ten. Ask children to draw nine objects (let the children each have a turn at drawing an object). Keep counting and recounting as another object is drawn. The last page can be a picture of a necklace with ten beads. Use the necklace made in activity 3 to count ten beads before it is drawn. (It may be a good idea to draw the string of the necklace for the children to draw their beads upon.)

Shape and space

Unit 3

Objectives:

Count reliably up to five everyday objects (extend to ten)

Say and use number names in order in familiar contexts

Use language such as 'circle' or 'bigger' to describe the shape and size of flat and solid shapes

Use words such as 'bigger' and 'smaller' to describe size

Use shapes to make pictures and patterns

Vocabulary:

2-d shapes, circle, triangle, square, rectangle, flat, straight, curved, corner

sort, match, the same, different, bigger, smaller

3-d shapes, cube, sphere, cylinder, top, bottom, face, edge, hollow, solid

pattern, model, describe

References:

National Numeracy Strategy pages 24-27

Curriculum Guidance for the Foundation Stage pages 69, 78-81

Session 1:

Resources:
A selection of 2-d shapes
Shape lotto (photocopiable sheets 10-12)
Tubs for sorting (labelled with pictures of 2-d shapes)
Gummed paper and scissors

Starter

Recite numbers from one to five and back. Count up to ten and back from ten. Sing 'One, two, buckle my shoe'. Then sing or read 'Ten in the bed'.

Main teaching activity

Sit the class in a circle. Put a selection of 2-d shapes in the middle of the floor. Hold up a circle. Ask if anyone knows what the name of the shape is. Explain that it is a circle. Repeat for three other key shapes. Ask a child to find a square. The child selects a shape. Talk about the main features of the shape - the number of sides, length of sides - are they the same? Has it got any corners? Are the sides straight or curved?

Group activities

1 Play shape lotto. When children begin the game, encourage them to respond to the questions in sentences. 'Who has this shape?' 'What is this shape?' 'This shape is a ...' 'Who has a square?' 'I have a square.'

2 Children sort 2-d shapes into four tubs labelled with pictures of shapes. (Make sure that the children understand the concept of sorting.)

3 Children cut the gummed paper into shapes to make pictures.

Plenary

Pick one of the children's pictures from activity 3. Discuss the shapes that have been used. 'How many circles are there?' 'How many squares?'

Session 2:

Resources:

Various tubs/boxes of 2-d and 3-d shapes

Squares in varying sizes and colours (preferably in laminated card to stick on the board)

Shape lotto (photocopiable sheets 10-12)

Selection of shapes and tubs for sorting (as used in session 1)

Large sheets of paper cut into triangles, circles, squares and rectangles

Gummed paper shapes

Shapes and paint for printing

Tom Thumb's Musical Maths (A & C Black)

Starter

Children sit in a circle. Give a child a number of shapes in a tub (less than ten) and get them to count the shapes out of the tub. Get another child to check by recounting. Make sure that the child touches each shape as it is counted. Give another child a tub containing a different amount and repeat the process.

Main teaching activity

On the board have a selection of squares of varying sizes and colours, and a circle. Tell the children to look carefully at the board. Ask: 'Are all the shapes the same?' 'What shapes can you see?' 'How are the shapes different?' Reinforce the idea that all the squares are the same shape but different sizes.

Group activities

1   Play shape lotto, as for session 1.

2   Sort shapes, as for session 1; extend sorting criteria to include size.

3   Give children large sheets of paper cut in the shape of circles, triangles, squares or rectangles for them to stick paper shapes or print onto (circle shapes onto a circular sheet, triangle shapes onto a triangular sheet, and so on).

Plenary

Hold up a shape, say a triangle. Ask: 'Is my shape a square?' The children explain how they know that it isn't a square, and why it is a triangle. Conclude by singing 'My hat it has three corners' or the shape song from *Tom Thumb's Musical Maths*.

Session 3:

Resources:

Set of five rabbit cards (photocopiable sheet 13)

A variety of everyday objects – balls, oranges, boxes, dice

Selection of 2-d and 3-d shapes

3-d shapes for printing

Paper and paint

Starter

Take five rabbit cards and place them on the board. Arrange them in a line. Count them. Ask: 'How many rabbits can you see?' Move the rabbits. How many rabbits can they see now? Count them. 'Yes, there are still five.' Ask children to close their eyes while you re-arrange them. 'How many rabbits are there now?' Repeat this, arranging the rabbits close together and spaced out in different corners of the board. (This activity begins to develop the concept that the number of objects remains constant regardless of its position.)

Main teaching activity

Children sit in a circle. Show them the 2-d shapes that have been discussed previously. Name them. Put them onto a piece of paper and label them '2-d shapes'. Now get the box of everyday objects. Discuss the properties of the items, for example a ball is round, curved, and so on, then give the item its 3-d name. Pick up the die. Ask: 'How many faces has it got?' (When counting the faces, mark each one as it is counted.) 'What shape are the faces?' 'Are the edges straight or curved?' 'This shape is called a cube.' 'These shapes are called 3-d shapes.' Put them onto a piece of paper and label them '3-d shapes'.

Group activities

1   Children have a selection of 2-d and 3-d shapes. A child takes one and says what it is. Discuss its properties. Use this opportunity to reinforce the correct mathematical vocabulary. Continue until all children have had a turn.

2   Children sort a selection of objects and shapes into 2-d and 3-d families.

3   Children use 3-d shapes to print. Use the printed paper to make cylinders and wrap boxes for a class display.

Plenary

Sort 2-d and 3-d shapes. Look at the similarity between a solid cube and an open box. Repeat using a solid cylinder and a cardboard cylinder (toilet roll tube). Use the words 'solid' and 'hollow'.

Session 4:

Resources:

Children's prints from session 3 and 3-d objects used for printing

Selection of 2-d and 3-d shapes to identify

3-d shapes to sort

Old boxes, packaging, glue and sticky tape for modelling

Starter

Count from one to ten. Explain: 'When we start to count, what number do we start with?' One. 'Today we are going to count up to ten, but we are not going to start at number one. We are going to start at number two.' Hold up two fingers, say 'two' then 'three' … up to ten. You will probably have to hold up the corresponding number of fingers or use cubes/pictures at first. If you use cubes, make sure that the number of cubes corresponds to the number being said.

Main teaching activity

Look at yesterday's prints. Identify which shape was used, for example, a cuboid. Look at the different prints caused by different faces. If it is not obvious you may wish to demonstrate by printing in front of the children and matching the faces. Use boxes/bricks and ask children to build a tower. Get them to include a cylinder. Which way up is best? Why?

Group activities

1   As for session 3.

2   Sort a variety of 3-d shapes using the following criteria: rolls/does not roll.

3   Provide a variety of boxes and packages for the children to make models.

Plenary

Use the children's models as points for discussion. What is their model? What shapes can the children see? Encourage them to identify 3-d shapes and use words such as 'top' and 'bottom'. Are there any faces? What shapes are they?

Session 5:

Resources:

Feely bag/box containing a variety of shapes

Shapes to hide on shape trail

Selection of shapes for sorting

Old boxes, packaging, glue and sticky tape for modelling

Starter

Count from one to ten. Start at any small number and count to ten (as in session 4).

Main teaching activity

Use a feely box containing a variety of shapes. Children take turns in choosing a shape, describing what they can feel and what shape they think it is. Encourage them to use the correct terminology. (I have found that by making the front of the feely box open, the rest of the class are engaged in the activity as they can either agree or disagree with the statements being made.)

Group activities

1   Hold a shape trail around the classroom. Give children a variety of shapes to look for. Children identify the object/shape with an adult.

2   Sort objects and shapes using criteria – 'has six faces'/ 'doesn't have six faces' (extend by specifying 'has square faces' or 'hollow/solid').

3   As for session 4.

Plenary

'I can see a ——— in the classroom.' Choose a shape. The children identify where that shape is in the classroom. They may know that they have used it in their model.

Counting and measures

Unit 4

Objectives:

Say and use number names in order in familiar contexts

Count reliably up to five objects (extend to ten)

Use 'more/less' or 'longer/shorter' to make direct comparisons

Vocabulary:

length, long, longest, longer than, short, shortest, shorter than, compare

Which?, find out, the same number, more, less, as many as

numerals one to ten, count on, count back, count up to

References:

National Numeracy Strategy pages 2-8, 22-23

Curriculum Guidance for the Foundation Stage pages 69, 74, 75, 78, 79

Session 1:

Resources:
Objects or toys (six) for counting
Large paper for drawing life-size outlines of children
Cubes/bricks
Unifix/Multilink cubes

Starter

Sing 'Five little speckled frogs'. Get six objects (toys). Arrange them in a group. Count them. Ask a child to come and count them. How many are there? Ask another child to come and count the toys but tell them to begin counting with a different toy. How many toys are there? Repeat, but keep reminding the children of the starting point. Explain that it doesn't matter which toy you start counting with, the number in the group (set) doesn't change.

Main teaching activity

Stand up and tell the class that they are going to find out who is the tallest and the shortest in the class. Choose a child to stand up. Discuss who is the tallest – you or the child - and how you know. Who is the shortest? Ask another child to stand up. Who is the tallest of the two children? Select other children and compare their heights.

Group activities

1   Children draw around the tallest/shortest member of their group. Discuss who they think is the tallest. Who is taller than them and who is shorter than them? Cut around the outline and use it as a talking point in the plenary.

2   Use cubes/bricks to build a tower that is the same height as a chair, a classroom toy or shorter than themselves.

3   Use Unifix/Multilink cubes to make three towers of different heights and order them (shortest to tallest).

Plenary

Look at the children's paper outlines. Ask the children to help you order them. Ask questions to reinforce today's vocabulary and use it to compare. Briefly discuss activities 2 and 3. During today children will probably equate height with age, relating it to their own experiences of younger children being smaller than them and older children taller. I always try to demonstrate that this is not the case by comparing two children of the same age.

Session 2:

Resources:

Container full of cubes

Two of each of the following (different lengths), for example pencils, socks, scarves, strips of paper, pieces of string

Snake shapes, long and short, for matching (photocopiable sheet 14)

Straws, string, scissors

Felt pens and paper

Pasta shapes/beads and laces/string (to make necklaces)

Starter

Sing 'One, two, three, four, five, once I caught a fish alive'. Count from one to ten and back.

Show the children a container full of cubes. Explain that you want them to help you count them into groups of five. Invite children to count out five and arrange them in a pattern. Repeat, but each time encourage the children to arrange the bricks in a different pattern, pointing out that there are still five in each arrangement. This activity gives the children experience of counting out objects from a larger group.

Main teaching activity

Put a selection of objects (two of each, different lengths) in the middle of the group. Pick up two pencils. Are they the same? If not, why not? Identify the differences using the vocabulary 'long' and 'short'. Make sets labelled 'long' and 'short'. Ask a child to find the two scarves, identify which is long and which is short and put them into the correct set. Repeat with other objects.

Group activities

1   Use photocopiable sheet 14 (long and short snakes). Pick a snake. Can they find a snake that is longer, shorter or the same length? You may find that the children identify other attributes.

2   Give each child a straw, a felt-tip pen and a piece of paper. Ask them to draw lines that are longer, shorter or the same length as the straw. See if they can cut a piece of string that is the same length.

3   Use pasta/beads to make long or short necklaces.

Plenary

Hold a selection of straws of different lengths (two each of the same length). Ask a child to select a straw. Another child selects a straw. Compare the two lengths. Repeat the activity until all the straws are used.

Session 3:

Resources:

Objects of different lengths (as for session 2)

Variety of ribbons/strips of paper in different lengths and widths

Fine/broad line felt tips

Labels: 'wide' and 'narrow'

Starter

Sing 'Ten green bottles'.

Main teaching activity

Children sit in a circle. Ask them to count from one to ten together. Next, ask them to take it in turns to say one number each. Start at one, point to the next child, who says 'two'; continue around the circle until ten is reached and begin again.

Group activities

In sessions 1 and 2 many activities and ideas have been introduced that can be further developed within the classroom. If the children have a sound understanding, other vocabulary such as 'wide', 'narrow', 'thick' and 'thin' may be introduced. This can be done by providing a wide range of objects, such as ribbons or strips of paper of differing lengths and widths that can be sorted and discussed.

Children can use different width felt pens to draw straight and wavy line patterns. Patterns can feature thick lines or fine lines or some children may combine the two widths.

Plenary

Discuss and review today's activities.

Session 4:

Resources:

Kipper's Toybox by Mick Inkpen (Hodder Children's Books)

Box containing up to ten objects

Containers for each child with variety of objects for counting

Sticky labels

Sand tray and objects to bury – shells, buttons, and so on (five of each kind)

Starter

Read *Kipper's Toybox*. Emphasise the way Kipper keeps recounting his toys. When he gets a different answer on the recount he realises that there is something wrong.

Main teaching activity

Introduce a box of objects to the class. Count out all of the toys. How many toys are there? Children use the last number counted. Recount the toys but deliberately make a mistake. Something is wrong. How many are there? What did you do wrong? Recount the objects together.

Group activities

1   Give children a box each containing a variety of counting objects. Children take it in turns to count out the objects. Ask how many they have got and write a label for their container. Let the children see you writing the number. (This is so they can see links with counting and numerals.)

2   Give children a variety of containers with objects in. Tell them that there should be five things in each container, but they have seen you make mistakes with your counting today - you might have made a mistake! They need to count how many things there are and then put five things in.

3   Children find buried objects in the sand tray. There should be five of each item. You may wish to put four of one object in.

Plenary

Discuss activity 2. Did they find any mistakes? What did they find out? Let some children count out their containers. Count out the objects found in the sand tray. Did they find all the objects? How many did they find?

Session 5:

Resources:

Set of dot cards, one to ten (photocopiable sheets 1 and 2)

Washing line and pegs

Set of large numeral cards (photocopiable sheets 3 to 6)

Containers for each child with variety of objects for counting (as for session 4)

Sticky labels

Sand tray and objects to bury (as for session 4)

Starter

Begin by singing 'One, two, buckle my shoe'.

Main teaching activity

Use the set of dot cards and ask children to order them on the washing line. Introduce the numerals. Children attach the numeral cards to the dot cards indicated by you. Count from one to ten, pointing to the numeral as each number is said.

Group activities

1   As for session 4.

2   As for session 4 but give the children a different target number (depending on the group).

3   Bury some objects in the sand tray for the children to find. Don't tell them how many items are buried, only that there are the same number of each item.

Plenary

Discuss how many things they found in the sand tray. How did they know that they had to keep looking for more objects? Look at the numerals that have been written today in activity 1. Can children match the numerals to those on the washing line?

Counting and adding (one more)

Unit 5

Objectives:

Begin to recognise 'zero' and 'none' in stories and rhymes

Find one more than (up to five objects, extend to ten)

Begin to recognise numerals one to five, then introduce zero

Vocabulary:

zero, none, count, count up to, count back from, before, after, more, less, find, next, bigger (than), more (than), smaller (than), less (than)

number, number line, one, two, three, four, five, six, seven, eight, nine, ten

References:

National Numeracy Strategy pages 2-8, 14-15

Curriculum Guidance for the Foundation Stage pages 68-69, 74-77

Session 1:

Resources:
Number line (photocopiable sheet 7) or 'Ten in the bed' (photocopiable sheet 15)
Large ladybird (laminated) and ten spots (photocopiable sheet 8); Blu-Tack
Numeral cards (photocopiable sheets 3-6)
Dot cards (photocopiable sheets 1-2)
Ladybird cards (photocopiable sheet 9)
Containers labelled with one to ten spots
Paper, rubber stamps and pictures to make group number books

Starter

Count from one to ten. Sing 'Ten in the bed'. Use a number line as a point of reference as you are counting up to ten and back (or the 'Ten in the bed' photocopiable sheet 15.)

Main teaching activity

Using the large ladybird, stick one spot onto it (using Blu-Tack). Ask the children how many spots they can see on the ladybird. Pick up another spot, hold it and say 'and one more'. Place this on the ladybird. 'How many spots are there now?' Two. Repeat this process, emphasising 'one more', until all ten spots are on the ladybird. Children may start predicting what number will come next.

Now remove the spots, counting back as each one is removed. Can they see any spots? No, there are none left. Ask the children to close their eyes whilst you arrange four spots. Tell them to open their eyes and say how many spots they see. Four. Say: 'I have one more spot. How many are there now?' Repeat using a variety of starting points.

Group activities

1   Play pairs (Pelmanism) using numeral and dot cards. This activity can be differentiated by using two sets of numeral cards to five or ten. Children can use dot cards and match to numeral cards or just match dots.

2   Use the ladybird cards. Children sort them into containers labelled with the corresponding number of spots.

3   Children use rubber stamps/pictures cut from catalogues to make sets of objects (a page for each numeral with corresponding pictures and a page for each dot pattern). When the books are made up these pages should face each other.

Plenary

Use the containers from activity 2. Take out a card. How many spots are there? Ask a child to put the corresponding number of spots on the large ladybird. Count them, and then add one more spot. How many spots are there now? Can they find a ladybird with that many spots? Continue until there are ten spots on the ladybird. Remove them one at a time, counting back until none remain.

Session 2:

Resources:
Ten caterpillars (photocopiable sheet 16), preferably laminated
Numeral cards and dot cards (for Pelmanism)
Sorting trays with numbers or dots in the base
Counters
Paper, rubber stamps and pictures to make group number books (as for session 1)

Starter

Sit the children in a circle and count together from one to ten. Next, you start the count but the children continue the count around the circle. When every child has had a turn, explain that you are going to say a number and point to someone. They have to say the next number. This ensures that all children are involved and paying attention. Point to another child who must say the next number. Repeat until everyone has had a turn.

Main teaching activity

Sing 'One caterpillar crawling up the wall, one caterpillar crawling up the wall. If one more joins him and starts crawling up the wall, there will be two caterpillars crawling up the wall' (to the tune of 'Ten green bottles'). Start with a clear board and talk your way through the song, adding and counting the caterpillars as you go. In other words, begin by asking: 'How many caterpillars are there?' None - zero. 'And one more makes one caterpillar'. Add one caterpillar. 'How many caterpillars are on the wall? One, and one more makes two.' Add another caterpillar. Continue until five are on the wall. Then remove the caterpillars. Begin to use numbers randomly. 'If there are four on the wall (put four on the wall) and one more crawls up, how many will there be?'

Group activities

1   As for session 1.
2   Put numerals or dots in the base of the sorting trays. Children put the corresponding number of counters into each tray.
3   As for session 1.

Plenary

Look at the pages that have been made for the book. Discuss how many pictures are on each page. Explain that the pages need to be put in the correct order. Ask the children to help you sequence the pages. End by singing 'One caterpillar ...'

Session 3:

Resources:
Ten caterpillars (as for session 2)
Washing line and pegs
Large numeral cards (zero to ten) or dot cards
Die and counters
Trays containing objects to count
Pictures to cut and stick or stamps
Paper, scissors, glue

Starter

Sing 'One caterpillar ...' Place the caterpillars on the board, one at a time, starting at zero. Ask a child to get another one, and put it on the board, saying 'There's one'. Ask another child to get 'another one'.

Main teaching activity

Show the children an empty washing line. Tell them that all the numbers are missing and you need their help to put them on the line. Start at zero and count up to ten. Put the numeral cards on the floor. (You may want to substitute dot cards for numerals.) Ask a child to come and find the card with zero on. Put it on the left-hand side of the washing line. 'What number comes next?' Number one. Ask another child to find the number one. This will be challenging for many of the children and they will need support to complete the number line. When complete, start at zero and count, pointing to the numerals as they are said.

Group activities

1   Roll a die. Children get that amount of counters and then one more. Ask: 'How many counters are there altogether?' Repeat several times. Children take turns rolling the die, getting the correct amount of counters and one more. When the children have all had two turns, count all of their counters.

2   Put out trays containing a variety of items. The children put 'one more' counter into each tray and then count how many items are in each tray.

3   Children use pictures or stamps to make a collection of items on a page.

Plenary

Children show the collection of items that they have printed or stuck onto paper. Count how many items there are. Ask a child to choose a rubber stamp or picture to add. Say: 'How many things did we count? Now we are going to add one more. How many are there now?' Repeat using several pictures.

Session 4:

Resources:
Washing line and pegs
Five little ducks (photocopiable sheet 17)
Large numeral cards
Unifix/Multilink cubes
Dot cards, counters and containers
Crayons, pencils, paper and drawing materials

Starter

Attach the number five numeral card to the middle of the washing line. Sing 'Five little ducks'. Point to the number five. Attach the number four to the left of the number five, as you sing about the four ducks. Continue until the zero is attached.

Main teaching activity

Children start at zero and count forward to ten and back to zero. Look at the numbers on the washing line. Count up to five, then ask 'What number comes after five?' A child then picks out the number six and attaches it to the washing line. Continue up to ten. Point to a number; say the number. Encourage the children to whisper the number. Ask questions, such as: 'What number comes after two?' 'What number comes before five?' Get the children to point in the direction (to the right for 'after', to the left for 'before').

Group activities

1 Give each child a cube. Hold one cube yourself and ask the child on your right 'How many cubes have you got?' One. 'I've got one cube as well. Let's put them together. One add one more makes two.' Give the tower of two to the child. Ask: 'Now how many cubes have you got?' Two. Ask the next child who has just one cube to make a combined tower of three. 'Two add one more is three'. Continue around the group until a tower of ten is achieved, explaining each time that the tower is passed on that somebody has added 'one more' cube.

2 Give children a selection of dot cards. They choose one card, get the corresponding number of counters and put them into a container along with the dot card. They then get one more counter and put it into the container. How many counters are there altogether? They will probably need to take them out and recount them. The children can then draw their own dot card with the new total.

3 Put a variety of pencils, crayons, pieces of paper and other drawing materials on a table. Tell the children that you were going to have three children drawing pictures of themselves at the table but you have decided to let one more join in. They need to make sure that everyone has a piece of paper, a crayon, and so on. (They will need to get 'one more' of everything.)

Plenary

Discuss activity 3. How did they solve the problem? Children bring the containers from activity 2. Take out the dot cards and check the number of counters, emphasising the amount on the original card, and saying 'and one more makes …'.

Session 5:

Resources:
Washing line and pegs
Numeral cards (two sets)
Cubes
Dot cards, counters and containers (as for session 4)
Four cups, plates, knives, forks and spoons

Starter

Sing 'One caterpillar …'.

Main teaching activity

Start counting from zero to ten. Begin the count again only this time get children to identify the corresponding numeral card and attach it to the washing line. Give each child a numeral card (differentiate by giving appropriate numbers). Point to a number and say the number. If anyone has that number, they stand up and show you their number. Repeat.

Group activities

1 Put a collection of cubes in the middle of the table. The children all take one cube and begin to make a staircase up to five cubes. Count up the staircase: 'One and one more makes two, two and one more makes three', and so on.

2 As for session 4.

3 Children set the table for three bears and a friend.

Plenary

As for session 4.

Assess and review

The National Numeracy Strategy has set aside two days per half term for assessment. However, continuous assessment is necessary to inform our day-to-day planning and delivery. With some children it is easy to state whether they have achieved the key objective or not, but you may be unsure about others and you can, therefore, use these two sessions to work alongside these children to gain an accurate assessment.

By the end of Unit 5, most children should be able to:

- Join in number rhymes
- Recite the number names to ten
- Use their fingers to help count up to ten
- Recite the number names back from ten
- Give one number name to each object (one-to-one correspondence)
- Count by pointing to or moving an object
- Begin to recognise 'none' and 'zero' in rhymes
- Begin to recognise numerals (zero to five, extending to ten)
- Add one more practically and recount
- Say the 'next' number
- Begin to count on from a small number
- Begin to realise that position/size doesn't affect the number counted
- Begin to realise that if a recount produces a different answer something is wrong
- Begin to realise that the order in which objects are counted doesn't affect the total

- Begin to use appropriate language to compare length

- Begin to use vocabulary related to 2-d and 3-d shapes, recognise and name some of these shapes

All of the above have been covered during the previous five units. It is important to remember that many of the statements say that children 'begin to' and these two words are very important. You need to keep in mind your class and provide the mathematical experiences at the appropriate level.

Remember that the information these assessments provide must be used to plan the children's activities at the appropriate level. This may mean revisiting, consolidating or extending the level at which the child is working.

Pages 13 to 15 of *Using Assess and Review Lessons* (DfES 0632/2001) provide examples of questions that can be used to assess a child's understanding against the key objectives.

Counting, comparing and ordering numbers

Unit 7

Objectives:

Say and use number names to ten in order in familiar contexts, for example number rhymes, songs and stories

Recite number names in order from one to 20

Use language such as 'more' or 'less', 'greater' or 'smaller' to compare two numbers up to five and say which is more or less

Vocabulary:

count, count in ones, start at, count on, count from

more, most, less, least, largest, smallest, compare

predict, guess, What comes next?, How many?, before, after, next

numbers zero to 20

References:

National Numeracy Strategy pages 2-8, 11-13

Curriculum Guidance for the Foundation Stage pages 68, 74, 75

Session 1:

Resources:

Twenty buttons or counters

Set of dominoes and a die

Outlines of two trees, apples and oranges cut from card/paper

Cubes, paper and crayons

Starter

Sit children in a circle. Count up to ten together. Put seven buttons on the floor. Ask how many buttons there are. Count them. Pick them up, then put ten buttons on the floor. 'Now how many buttons are there?' Count them. Increase the number of buttons by one, enabling the numbers up to 20 to be introduced.

Main teaching activity

Begin with the outline of two trees. Put three oranges on one tree and an apple on the other. Count how many oranges there are. Count how many apples there are. Say: 'There are more oranges than apples. There are less apples than oranges'. Ask how many oranges there would be if you put one more on the tree. If you put one more apple on the tree, how many apples would there be? Repeat using different amounts of oranges and apples and ask which tree has more or less.

Group activities

1   Put a set of dominoes face down. Children take it in turns to roll a die and turn over a domino. How many spots can they count on the die? How many spots are on the domino? If there are more on the domino, the child keeps the domino. If there are less, the domino is returned, face down. The first child to collect five dominoes is the winner.

2   Children make a tower of four cubes. They then make another tower using more than four cubes and one using less.

3   Children draw two vases and add different numbers of flowers in each.

Plenary

Discuss activities 2 and 3. Emphasise the words 'more' and 'less' by comparing the number of flowers in the vases and the number of cubes in the towers.

Session 2:

Resources:

Glove puppet for starter (optional)

A large piece of paper divided into ten columns

Small squares of paper (25 in one colour to use in columns 1, 3, 5, 7, 9; and 30 of another colour)

Cubes

Small items to bury in the sand tray with corresponding labelled sheets for sorting

Starter

All the class count together up to ten. Explain that you are going to count with them for part of the way, but when you stop counting you want them to carry on. Start at one, stop counting at seven, the children continue up to ten. Repeat, stopping at six. Next time, tell the children that you want them to listen carefully whilst you count. Say that you may forget how to count, so if you stop you want them to say the next numbers. (I have found using a glove puppet works really well for this activity.) Count up to eight, the children say nine and ten. Repeat this activity several times. Try giving the children three consecutive numbers and see if they can continue the count.

Main teaching activity

Use squares of paper to make a staircase pattern on a large piece of paper divided into ten columns. Put one square in the lower left-hand corner of the paper. Then next to it place two squares of paper. 'How many squares can they count in this column?' One. 'How many are in the next column?' Two. Ask whether anyone can guess or predict how many squares you are going to put in the next column. Why do they think it is going to be three? Can they see a pattern? Which is the biggest/largest number? Which is the smallest number? Continue building the staircase until ten squares are in the final column.

Group activities

1   Make staircases with the children (as above) only vary the size of step.

2   Children use cubes to make a staircase, starting at one.

3   Bury some sorting items in the sand. Label sheets of paper to enable the children to sort the items, for example a picture of a button, a cube. Children find the objects and then draw a set containing more buttons, cubes, and so on.

Plenary

Discuss activity 3. 'How many buttons did you find in the sand?' 'How many did you draw?' 'Are there more buttons here or in the drawing?' Repeat using different objects. End by using a staircase. 'Is three more than one?' 'Which is the biggest number, five or two?' Check by counting.

Session 3:

Resources:

Cups, straws and cubes

Two sets of numeral cards, initially to five

Set of dominoes

Large dot cards

Sticky notes with numerals zero to five written on (extend to ten if appropriate)

Washing line

Starter

Sing 'One, two, three, four, five, once I caught a fish alive'. Recap on yesterday's starter. Begin by giving the children three consecutive numbers. Can they continue the count? For example, you say 'one, two, three', the children continue 'four, five, six' and so on, up to ten. You say 'three, four, five' and the children continue 'six, seven' up to ten. Repeat starting at different numbers. Can the children continue the count when only two numbers are given, for example 'four, five'? Can they continue the count when only one number is given?

Main teaching activity

Put three cups out on the table and four straws. Explain: 'We are going to find out whether there are more cups or straws. Let's count them. There are four straws and three cups. Four is more than three.' Check the statement by matching one to one. Show the children eight red cubes and six blue cubes. 'Are there more red or blue? Let's count them.' 'Which is more, eight or six? Let's check by matching the cubes one to one.'

Group activities

1   Put two sets of numeral cards face down. Children take it in turns to turn over two cards and say which number is more.

2   Children sort dominoes into two sets by counting spots, for example more than four spots/less than four spots.

3   Let the children work together to order large dot cards on the washing line. Children attach sticky notes to corresponding dot cards

Plenary

Discuss activities 2 and 3.

Session 4:

Resources:

Counting Rhymes by John Foster (Oxford University Press)

Large numeral or dot cards and a die

3 x 2 grids with a selection of numbers written on - one to nine (you may wish to differentiate when giving these to the children – have some grids with numbers less than six, some may need dots to support them)

A die and counters

Cubes made into towers

Pots labelled 'more than' and 'less than'

Dominoes

Sheets of A4 paper divided in two to represent blank dominoes

Starter

Recite 'One, two, three, four' (from *Counting Rhymes*). Hold up three fingers. Ask the children to hold up *more than* three fingers. Hold up five fingers. Ask the children to hold up *more than* five fingers. Repeat using up to nine fingers.

Main teaching activity

Display the large numeral or dot cards. Roll a die. Ask a child to find the corresponding card. Can the children tell you a number that is larger? Let them find the corresponding card.

Group activities

1   Give each child a 3 x 2 grid with a selection of numbers one to nine written on it. Children take turns to roll a die. If they roll a three, for example, the child looks at their grid and finds a number larger than three and covers it with a counter. Repeat.

2   Children have a variety of cubes made into towers. Give each child two containers labelled 'more than' and 'less than' and a target number, for example three. They sort the towers into the appropriate containers.

3   Children choose a domino and make a large domino (using the A4 paper divided in two) with more spots.

Plenary

Choose a domino. Ask children to find dominoes from activity 3 that have more spots. Discuss activity 2.

Session 5:

Resources:

Counting Rhymes by John Foster (Oxford University Press)

Large piece of paper and squares (as for session 2)

3 x 2 grids, a die and counters (as for session 4)

Cubes

Numeral cards or dot cards

Starter

Recite 'One, two, three, four' (from *Counting Rhymes*). Hold up four fingers. Ask the children to hold up *less than* four fingers. Hold up six fingers. Ask the children to hold up *less than* six fingers. Repeat this using up to ten fingers.

Main teaching activity

As for session 2 but start with ten squares in column 1, then nine in column 2. Look at the pattern. Can anyone predict what number will come next? Place the squares in column 3, saying 'One less than nine is eight'. Continue across the grid.

Group activities

1   As for session 4 but child finds a number that is smaller.

2   Children make a staircase starting with five cubes.

3   Give children a set of numeral or dot cards and ask them to order them, starting at zero up to five (extend if appropriate) and then arrange in descending order.

Plenary

Start at five and count back. Look at activity 2. Count back in ones starting at five, checking that the correct amount is in each tower. Count up to ten and then attempt to count back. Discuss activity 3.

Counting, adding and subtracting

Unit 8

Objectives:

Recite number names in order from one to 20 and beyond

Count reliably more than five objects

Find one more and one less than a number up to nine

Vocabulary:

number, numbers one, two, three ... 20

count, How many?, count up to, count back from, start with, start at, before, add, after, How many altogether?

more than, less than, bigger than, smaller than

References:

National Numeracy Strategy pages 2-8, 14-15

Curriculum Guidance for the Foundation Stage pages 68-69, 74-77

Session 1:

Resources:

Bean bag

Ten large laminated caterpillars (photocopiable sheet 16) and Blu-Tack

Numeral cards (zero to five) and tray of cubes

Selection of dominoes or dot cards and paper, crayons, glue

Paper plates labelled with dots and numerals up to the value of five

Playdough

Starter

Sit the children in a circle. Count from one up to ten, then from one up to 20 together. Tell the children that you want them to count around the circle. Show them the bean bag. The child holding the bean bag says 'one', then passes it to the next child who says 'two'. Continue passing the bean bag around the circle, counting up to 20.

Main teaching activity

Show the children one caterpillar. Stick it to the board (with Blu-Tack). 'How many caterpillars are there?' 'I have got one more caterpillar.' Stick it to the board. Say: 'One add one more makes two. How many caterpillars are there now?' Two. 'I am going to put one more onto the board.' Stick on the caterpillar: 'Two add one more makes three'. Continue, repeating the process until all ten caterpillars are on the board.

Group activities

1   Take a set of numeral cards (zero to five, but extend if appropriate), shuffle them and put them face down in a pile. Put a tray of cubes in the middle of the table. Ask a child to turn over a card and identify the number. The child makes a tower with the corresponding number of cubes. Ask 'How many cubes have you got?' Then: 'Can you get me one more? Now how many cubes have you got?' Encourage the children to say out loud 'Six and one more is seven'. The next child turns over a card. Repeat.

2   Put out a selection of dominoes or dot cards. Children count the number of dots, draw or stick the corresponding number of spots onto a sheet of paper, then pick a different colour and draw one more spot.

3   Children choose a paper plate (labelled with dots and numerals up to five). Count the dots (or some children may be able to recognise the number). Use playdough to make the corresponding amount of cakes, then make one more.

Plenary

Discuss activity 3. How many cakes did they have to make? Count the dots and point to the numeral. Count the cakes, stopping when you have reached that number. 'You had to make one more. Well done. I can see that you made one more, so ... and one more makes ... altogether.' Discuss activity 2.

Session 2:

Resources:

Large numeral cards zero to ten and washing line

'Ten in the bed' (photocopiable sheet 15)

Set of numeral cards and tray of cubes

Peg boards and pegs

Paper plates and playdough (as for session 1)

Starter

Count from zero to ten, then zero to 20 together. Show the children the large numeral cards and identify the numbers. Put them on the floor, randomly. Begin to count. 'Zero.' Ask a child to find zero and peg it to the washing line. 'What number comes after zero?' One. Ask a child to find the number one; continue up to ten. Choose children to answer the questions carefully: identifying the larger numbers will provide a challenge for some whereas simply stating what number comes next will be a challenge for others.

Main teaching activity

Using the pictures from the 'Ten in the bed' photocopiable sheet, begin to recite the song: 'There were ten in the bed and the little one said, "Roll over".' Ask a child to either remove or cover up a teddy. 'How many teddies were there?' Ten. 'How many has ... covered up?' One. 'One less than ten is ... nine.' (You will have to count all the teddies.) 'There are nine teddies in the bed.' Ask another child to remove or cover up a teddy. 'There were nine teddies. ... has covered up one. One less than nine is ...' Repeat until no teddies remain. Refer to the washing line. Start at ten and count back to zero.

Group activities

1   Take a set of numeral cards (zero to five, but extend if appropriate), shuffle them and put face down in a pile. Put a tray of cubes in the middle of the table. Ask a child to turn over a card and identify the number. The child makes a tower with the corresponding number of cubes. Ask: 'How many cubes have you got?' (For example, six.) Tell the child to break one cube off the tower. 'Now how many cubes are in the tower?' Five. Encourage the child to respond, saying 'One less than six is five'. The next child turns over a card. Repeat.

2   Using a peg board: children begin with five pegs on the left-hand side of the board. Their task is to put the next line of pegs on the board but one less: 'One less is four'. Continue arranging the pegs so they reduce in number by one. (You may find that some children can begin with a number higher than five.)

3   Children use the paper plates as in session 1, yesterday. They make the corresponding number of cakes and then take one away and put it on a separate plate.

Plenary

Discuss activity 3. 'How many cakes did you make?' Count them. 'Then you had to take one cake away. How many cakes were left?' 'So one less than ... is ...' . Show the group the peg board. Look at the step pattern created. Use a board that starts with six pegs and count: 'One less than six is five, one less than five is four'.

Session 3:

Resources:

Cubes, to include five per child of the same colour

Starter

Sing 'One man went to mow'. Give each child five Unifix cubes (one colour per child). Hold up one cube and ask the children to hold up one cube. Hold up two cubes made into a tower. 'How many cubes are in my tower?' Count them. Ask the children to make a tower of two and hold it in the air. Continue until a tower of five is shown. Keep asking children to make and hold up towers of randomly chosen numbers between one and five. Ask children to make different towers, for example: 'If you have red cubes, make a tower of three'. 'If you have blue cubes, make a tower of four' and so on.

The concepts of 'one more' and 'one less' can be difficult for children to grasp. You may need to consolidate the previous two sessions by repeating activities. However, if you feel the children need a challenge you may wish to use both concepts.

Main teaching activity and group activities

As for session 1 or 2.

Plenary

Count up to ten and back. Put out three cubes. Can the children tell you what is one more and one less than three?

Put out five cubes. 'What is one more/one less?' Hold up four fingers. 'What is one more/one less?'

Count up to ten as follows: 'One and one more is two, two and one more is three, three and one more is four', and so on. Count back: 'Ten and one less is nine, nine and one less is eight', and so on.

Session 4:

Resources:
Large numeral cards zero to ten and washing line
Tray of cubes
Satsumas
Dominoes
Paper and paint (green and purple) for printing

Starter
Sit children in a horse-shoe shape. Count from zero to 20. Put the large numeral cards on the floor in a random order. Ask one child to find zero and attach it to the washing line. 'What number comes after zero?' One. Ask another child to get the number one and attach it to the washing line. Continue until all the cards are on the washing line. As you point to the cards, encourage the children to hold up the corresponding number of fingers. 'Zero and one more makes one.' Children hold up one finger. 'One and one more makes … (children unfold one finger) two.' Continue up to ten. Emphasise the word 'more'. Ask questions: 'What is one more than two?' 'What is one more than four?' and so on. You can reverse the procedure counting back from ten with the children folding down their fingers. Emphasise the word 'less'.

Main teaching activity
Put six cubes in the middle of the horse shoe. Ask: 'How many cubes are there?' Children count as you move them. Repeat using seven, eight and then nine cubes, moving the cubes into a line and recounting them. When they have been counted, show the children the large numeral card for six. Ask a child to match the card with six cubes. Repeat using the numbers seven, eight and nine.

Group activities
1   Show the children a satsuma, then peel it. Separate it into segments. Ask: 'How many segments are there?' Count the segments. Let the children have one satsuma between two and count how many segments are in their satsuma. Act as scribe to record the numbers. Discuss the amounts. Can they say who had the smallest/largest number of segments?

2   Find dominoes with totals of six or seven.

3   Make thumb print pictures. Use either green or purple paint and make bunches of grapes containing six, seven, eight or nine.

Plenary
Discuss activity 3. Count how many grapes are in each bunch. 'Which bunch has got the most grapes?' 'Which bunch has the least number or fewest?' (Some children may have found the counting difficult because they were unable to touch or move the grapes so it is an opportunity to model a systematic way of counting objects.)

Session 5:

Resources:
Counting Rhymes by John Foster (Oxford University Press)
Large numeral cards and washing line
Plain biscuits, icing, cake decorations (small sweets, silver dragees)
Set of dominoes
Circular pieces of paper and pencils/crayons

Starter
Say the rhyme 'One little kitten' (in Counting Rhymes). Count up to ten and back. Put the large numeral cards on the floor in a random order. Ask one child to find the number ten and hang it on the right-hand side of the washing line. 'What is one less than ten?' Nine. Ask a child to find the number nine and hang it on the line. (The children will need considerable support at this stage in finding and recognising the numbers.) Repeat until all the cards have been attached.

Main teaching activity
Point to the number four. Ask: 'What is one less than four?' Show four fingers. Fold one down. 'One less than four is three.' Point to the numbers. Repeat, saying: 'One less than five is … ?' 'One less than three is … ?' 'What is one more than two?' 'One more than four?' Try to get the children to begin to understand that one more is the number after, and one less is the number before.

Group activities
1   Using a plain biscuit, get the children to count out eight small edible items to decorate their biscuit. Put icing onto the biscuits and let the children count each decoration as they put it onto their biscuit. Ask them to get one more. How many decorations have they got now? When all the biscuits are complete, put them onto plates to be used in the plenary.

2   Find dominoes with totals of eight or nine.

3   Using circular pieces of paper as plates, children draw different amounts of cakes. You will need to make sure that there is at least one of each number up to ten.

Plenary
Begin by discussing activity 1. 'How many sweets did we put on each biscuit?' Nine. 'How many biscuits are on this plate?' Count them (say ten). Let each child take one biscuit, and as they do, say 'Ten and one less is (count the remaining biscuits) nine; nine and one less is …' (count the remaining biscuits). As children become more confident, they will begin to predict what the next number will be, so count the biscuits as a check. Using the cake drawings from activity 3, order the plates starting with ten - 'and one less is nine'… 'and one less is eight' and so on, completing the sequence with an empty circle.

Shape, space and reasoning

Unit 9

Objectives:

Recite number names to 20

Name solid 3-d shapes

Put sets of objects in order of size

Use everyday words to describe position

Talk about and recognise simple symmetrical patterns

Vocabulary:

number, number names, count up to, one, two, three, four, five, six, seven, eight, nine, ten, 11, 12, 13, 14, 15, 16, 17, 18, 19, 20, before, after

position, in, on, under, below, above, between, next to, on top of, underneath, where?, big, small, middle, bigger, smaller

same, pattern, symmetrical, fold, half, both, match, matches, one side, other

shape, cube, pyramid, sphere, cone, circle, triangle, square, flat, curved, straight, round, size, side, top, bottom, solid, face, edge, corner

References:

National Numeracy Strategy pages 24-27,18-19

Curriculum Guidance for the Foundation Stage pages 68-69, 74-75, 78-81

Session 1:

Resources:

Large laminated ladybird, circular and square-shaped spots and Blu-Tack
Pegs and peg boards for pattern making
Small mirrors
Butterfly outlines (photocopiable sheet 18), coloured and cut in half
Paint and paper for blob printing
Pictures of butterflies

Starter

Children sit in a circle. Count up to ten around the circle. You may need to do this several times so that each child has a turn. Starting at zero, count up to 20 together then begin to count around the circle up to 20.

Main teaching activity

Explain that today you are going to look at patterns and symmetry. Begin by showing the children the ladybird. Start with four spots and arrange them, two on each side, so that the ladybird is symmetrical. Say: 'Both sides are the same'. Next, use six spots in total, three on each side in a random pattern. Get the children to re-arrange the spots so that the design is the same on both sides.

Put a selection of square and circular spots up on the board. Arrange them so that the pattern on both sides is the same. Next put a design on the board that is not symmetrical. Ask whether the pattern is the same on both sides. Ask a child to move a spot until the design is symmetrical. Arrange one side of the pattern on the board and children take it in turns to create the matching half.

Group activities

1   Using pegs and peg boards, choose one peg and put it in the top left-hand corner of your board. The children copy on their own board. Now add several pegs to the left-hand side of your board. The children copy this. Use a mirror to reflect the peg pattern. Children have a go at creating the mirrored pattern on their board. Give them the opportunity to use small mirrors to reflect their own peg board designs.

2   Children match correct halves of the butterflies.

3   Look at some pictures of butterflies and see how the patterns are symmetrical. Let children fold a piece of paper in half (approximately), unfold the paper and choose which side they are going to put the paint on. Show them how to put several large blobs of paint on, then fold the paper. Press down so that the paint transfers to the other side. Unfold the paper.

Plenary

Discuss activity 2. Put some incorrect halves together. Ask 'Is this picture correct? Why not?' Choose another incorrect half. Get children to explain/describe the correct half that is needed.

Session 2:

Resources:

Where's Spot? by Eric Hill or *Where, Oh Where, is Kipper's Bear?* by Mick Inkpen

Selection of toys for positional vocabulary

Enlarged copies of tree and animal cards plus 6 A4 copies for children (photocopiable sheets 19 and 20)

Photocopied outlines of tables and boxes

Dolls' house/road/rail layout

Starter

Read *Where's Spot?* or *Where's Kipper's Bear?*

Main teaching activity

Refer back to the story. Ask the children who or what they were looking for in the story. Where did they look? Emphasise the positional vocabulary that they use. Explain that they are going to use some of those words to answer your questions. Put a toy on the table. 'Where is the toy? It is on the table.' Put the toy on the floor, under the chair, and so on, and encourage the children to respond to the question: 'Where is the toy?' Ask children to put the toy in a variety of locations specified by you. Let the children now ask the question 'Where is the toy?'

Group activities

1   You need enlarged copies of the tree and animal cards. Choose one card and place it in the middle row. Place the cat above it. Where is the cat? Place the bear next to the cat. Where is the bear? Continue until all six cards are used. Give children their own copy of the tree and six cards. Give them precise instructions on where to place the various characters, for example, 'Put the bear at the top of the tree'. When all six cards are used, ask the children to answer questions: 'Where is the monkey?' 'Who is next to …?'

2   Draw an outline of a table and a box and make copies for the group. Using pictures from old catalogues children cut and stick pictures in, on, under or next to the box and table.

3   Let children play with a dolls' house and/or rail/road layout to enable them to use and develop positional vocabulary.

Plenary

Discuss two pictures created in activity 2. Using equipment from activity 3 begin with a general discussion about the position of furniture, cars, and so on. Ask a child to instruct another child to position an object, for example 'Put the car in the garage'. Reinforce by asking 'Where is the car?' Repeat to give several children the opportunity to take part.

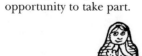

Session 3:

Resources:

Washing line and numeral cards

Selection of objects - two of each, one big, one small, for example balls, crayons, books, cups, plates

Boxes in different sizes

Russian dolls or stacking beakers (optional)

Construction toys

Starter

Count from zero to ten together. Using a washing line, put zero on the left. 'What number comes after zero?' One. Attach the one to the line. 'Which number comes after one?' Two. Attach the number two. Repeat up to number ten. Ask questions, such as 'Which number comes after …?' Repeat. Emphasise the key word *after*.

Main teaching activity

Make sure that the children are familiar with the story of 'Goldilocks and the three bears' or 'The three billy goats gruff'. Take two objects (different in size). Ask the children to say how the two objects are different. One is big and one is small. (You may want to use objects from the story as prompts.) Identify which is the biggest, which is the smallest. Introduce a medium-sized object. Where should this object go?

Group activities

1   Pick two boxes and discuss which is the biggest and which is the smallest. Put the smallest box inside the biggest. Take the box out, then introduce a third box. Discuss which box will fit inside each one. Then introduce a fourth box. If you have access to a set of Russian dolls or stacking beakers you may find these useful.

2   Use three boxes of different sizes. Label with pictures of the three bears or billy goats gruff. Children sort items appropriate to size for each of the characters.

3   Children use construction toys to make a bed, bench, table, and so on for the three characters.

Plenary

Discuss the objects made in activity 3. Which character was it made for? The biggest/smallest? Take some of the items from activity 2 and match them to the characters.

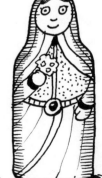

Session 4:

Resources:

Large numeral cards and washing line

Selection of 2-d and 3-d shapes (empty boxes and packets) to investigate and use for models

Rectangular sheets of paper

Starter

Children sit in a circle. Count from zero to ten and back all together. Put numeral card ten on the right-hand side of the washing line. 'Which number comes before ten?' Nine. Attach the number nine to the left of the number ten. Repeat until zero is attached. Ask questions, such as 'Which number comes before ...?' Repeat. Emphasise the key word *before.*

Main teaching activity

Put a selection of 2-d and 3-d shapes in the middle of the group. Recap on the terms 2-d and 3-d shapes. Ask children to identify a square. Can they see a 3-d shape with a square face? How many faces does it have? How many corners has it got? Are all the faces square? Can they see a 3-d shape with any circular faces?

Group activities

1   Can they use a rectangular piece of paper to make a cylinder?

2   Open up 3-d shapes and investigate the shapes that they can see.

3   Children build models using 3-d shapes.

Plenary

Discuss what the children have discovered.

Session 5:

Resources:

Large numeral cards and washing line

2-d shapes in different sizes

Rectangular sheets of paper (one for each child)

Shape templates, paper, pencils, crayons, glue

Starter

Count from one to 20 together. Count from zero to ten and back. Recap on sessions 3 and 4. The important words are 'before' and 'after'. Using the washing line, attach the zero. 'Which number comes after zero?' One. Attach one. Attach number ten to the opposite end of the washing line. 'Which number comes before number ten?' Nine. Attach number nine. 'Which number comes after number one?' Continue, alternating between each end of the number line. When the number line is complete, ask different questions, for example 'Which number comes after number three?' 'Which number comes before five?'

Main teaching activity

Children sit in a circle. Give all the children a 2-d shape. Hold up a shape, then say its name. 'Who has got a shape like this?' Ask them to hold up a shape with three sides or a curved side.

Group activities

1   Give each child a rectangular sheet of paper. Fold the paper. Discuss the shapes that can be made.

2   Children draw around three or four different sized squares or circles. Cut them out and order according to size. Stick onto paper.

3   Choose one shape of two different sizes. How many can they draw on their piece of paper?

Plenary

Discuss today's activities. Can the children order a set of rectangles, smallest to largest?

Measures, including time

Unit 10

Objectives:

Count reliably up to ten objects

Begin to use the vocabulary of time

Sequence familiar events

Use language to make comparisons of two quantities - more/less, heavier/lighter, full/empty

Vocabulary:

count, find, show, number, How many?, one, two, three, four, five, six, seven, eight, nine, ten

time, day, night, dark, morning, afternoon, week, Saturday, Sunday, Monday, Tuesday, Wednesday, Thursday, Friday, before, after, clock, next

Today is ..., yesterday, tomorrow

full, empty, half full, holds more, holds less, guess, pour, fill, nearly, almost, feel, heavy, light, heavier than, lighter than, balance, scales

References:

National Numeracy Strategy pages 22-23

Curriculum Guidance for the Foundation Stage pages 69-70, 78-79

Note: During this week, take photographs of the children doing various activities for sequencing and making a timetable.

Session 1:

Resources:

Ten plastic bottles or cardboard cut-outs numbered one to ten
Peace at Last by Jill Murphy (Macmillan)
Selection of day and night pictures for sorting
Paper divided into three (one per group or one per child depending upon organisation)
Pictures (or sequential jigsaws) to sequence
Black/dark blue/white paper, paints, pencils/crayons

Starter

Sing 'Ten green bottles' (use plastic bottles or cardboard cut-out shapes numbered one to ten as visual prompts). Count out all ten bottles. Check that the numbers are in the correct order (compare to a number line or frieze). Count up to ten and then back from ten, pointing to the corresponding bottles.

Read *Peace at Last* to the children. Talk about the pictures and ask questions, for example 'What time of day is it?' How do they know? (night time, they can see stars, moon, lights and so on) Put out a selection of day and night pictures so all the children are able to see them. Write two labels: 'day' and 'night'. Children take turns to choose a picture and say whether it should go in the day or night set.

Main teaching activity

Discuss what the children do before they come to school. When they are at school, what do they do? Begin to get the children to try and order their ideas by using phrases, for example 'What do we do when we get to school?' 'Yes, we hang our coats up.' 'What do we do next, after that?' 'Do we have our drink before we go out to play?' and so on. Discuss what they do when they go home.

Group activities

1 Divide a piece of paper into three sections (you may wish to create a group display or give each child an individual piece of paper). Label the sections: 'Before school', 'At school' and 'After school'. Ask children to draw pictures of themselves doing activities at the different times of day. Cut them out and sequence as a group to create an overview of a child's day.

2 Children work with an adult to discuss and sequence pictures (or jigsaws).

3 Using dark blue/black/white paper children draw or paint day/night pictures.

Plenary

Discuss the pictures created from activity 1. Is there anything that everyone does? Focus on the activities at school. What things happen at the same time every day? (playtime, lunch time) Ask the children to try to remember what they do when they go home after school for tomorrow's lesson.

Session 2:

Resources:

Containers (one per child) with ten cubes of the same colour

Paper divided into three sections (one per group or one per child depending upon organisation)

Pictures to sequence

Black/dark blue/white paper, paints, crayons

Starter

Count from one to ten and back. Give each child a container with ten cubes of the same colour. Say a number, for example, two. The children make a tower of two and hold it up. Repeat using numbers up to ten.

Main teaching activity

Ask the children to take turns describing what they did yesterday when they got home. Point out the elements that are common to all the children - eating tea, brushing teeth, going to bed. Other activities, such as watching television or going to visit friends may have been experienced by several children but not by the whole group. Are there things that they did yesterday after school that they know they will do again today? Are there things that happened at school yesterday they know will happen today? Can they tell you some of them? What about tomorrow?

Group activities

1 As for session 1.

2 As for session 1.

3 As for session 1.

Plenary

Discuss the pictures painted today and yesterday in activity 3. Ask questions about what or who they can see and what they are doing. Can they see the sun, moon or stars in the picture? Choose three pictures from activity 2 and sequence them. Put them in the wrong order. Ask which picture should come first. Why? Which picture should come next?

Session 3:

Resources:

Harlequin (A & C Black)

Flash cards showing days of the week

Mr Wolf's Week by Colin Hawkins (Mammoth)

Paper and drawing materials

Time related/sequential jigsaws and puzzles

Starter

Sing 'Each day different' (from *Harlequin*) or recite a rhyme about the days of the week, for example 'Solomon Grundy'. Recite the days of the week. Show the flash cards as you say the day. Say the days again, encouraging the children to join in. How many days are there in a week? Repeat the days of the week, holding up a finger every time a day is said. At the end, count how many fingers are being held up. 'How many days have I said?' Seven. 'Let's say the days again and this time you can help count by holding up your fingers.' Ask if anyone knows what day today is. Write on the board 'Today is ...'.

Main teaching activity

Read *Mr Wolf's Week*. Mr Wolf does a variety of activities throughout the week and wears different outfits. Make a list of the activities he does (use pictures) and match them to the days of the week. Discuss with the children activities that they do at school and on what day.

Group activities

1 Make a display:

	Morning	Lunchtime	Afternoon
Monday			
Tuesday			
Wednesday			
Thursday			
Friday			

If you have taken photographs of the children doing various activities during the week, you can add these later.

2 Children draw pictures about the Mr Wolf story to be used in a class book.

3 Introduce time-related or sequential jigsaws.

Plenary

Children talk about the pictures they have drawn. What is Mr Wolf doing? What day did he do that? Label the picture with the correct day of the week. Point to the area on the timetable to provide a cue. Ask 'What do we do on Monday?' then become more specific: 'What do we do on Monday morning?'

Session 4:

Resources:

Containers (one per child) with ten cubes in

Two carrier bags with shopping in - two of each item - distributed unevenly so that one bag weighs considerably more than the other

Pan balances, parcels of varying sizes containing sand, rice, cereals, tins, and so on, wrapped in a variety of coloured paper (These will be used to compare heavy/light so try not to relate size and weight.)

Plasticene or playdough

Starter

Count from one to ten and back. Give each child a container with ten cubes in. Say a number, children make a tower of cubes to match and hold up the tower. Repeat.

Main teaching activity

Begin by explaining that you have two important words that you want them to remember: 'heavy' and 'light'. Show the children the two carrier bags with your shopping in. Ask a child to come to the front of the class. Get them to stand with their arms out to the side and keep them straight. Give them the two carrier bags. Which one is heavy? Repeat and point, saying 'This one is heavy, so this one is light'. Ask: 'What happened when I gave you the heavy bag? Your arm went down'. Show the children a balance. Put in a heavy object and watch the pan go down. Pass the bags around the group. Ask: 'Which is heavy? If that bag is heavy, the other bag is …'.

Group activities

1   Put a selection of packages on the table. Children take turns in picking up two parcels and identifying which one is heavy and which one is light. Ask them to check their decision using pan balances. Look at the size of the parcels. Are the large parcels always heavy?

2   Give children the chance to use pan balances. Give them an object and ask them to find a parcel that is the same weight.

3   Give the children some Plasticene or playdough. Make sure that they all have the same amount. Ask them to make a model using all of their own Plasticene.

Plenary

Show the children two parcels. Ask them to predict which is the heaviest. How can they find out? Is the largest parcel always the heaviest? Look at the models made in activity 3. Discuss the differences in size, shape and thickness. Remind the children that they all had the same amount of Plasticene. Refer to activity 2, where the children had to make the pans balance. Check several parcels and corresponding objects to see if they balance. Ask a child to be a balance and hold the two carrier bags. Which is the heavy bag? See if they can make the two bags balance, by moving objects from one bag to the other. Check by emptying the objects out of the bag. They should contain the same objects.

Session 5:

Resources:

Plastic containers (preferably clear), plastic jugs, funnels, empty squash bottles, water tray, tea set

Access to sand and water trays

Salt dough recipe (photocopiable sheet 21) and ingredients (flour, salt, water)

Empty boxes and packets with a variety of dry materials to fill them - rice, pasta, lentils

Starter

Sing 'Ten full bottles' (to the tune of 'Ten green bottles'). Ask children to close their eyes and imagine they can see a wall. Now you want them to stand five bottles on the wall. Can they see the bottles on the wall in their head? (This skill of visualising is important to develop.) 'Let's count them: one, two, three, four, five.' Make one bottle fall. 'How many can you see standing on the wall now?' Count them. Repeat until all the bottles have fallen.

Main teaching activity

Today, there are two more important words you want them to remember: 'full' and 'empty'. Show the children a variety of familiar containers. Ask them to guess which container will hold more. (Remember, it is not essential to use water - sand or rice works just as well.) Children also need access to the sand and water trays to play in and investigate by pouring, filling and emptying containers. Show the children two containers at a time. Show them that they are empty. There is nothing in them. Tell them that you are going to fill the container carefully. When it is full, show the children. Emphasise the word 'full'. What would happen if you put any more in? Show the children the full container. Say: 'This container is full'. Show them the empty container. 'This container is empty.' 'Now I am going to pour the water into the other container. Which holds more?'

Group activities

1   Make salt dough using the recipe sheet. The cups must be full and the same size. (If a small cup is used then each child can make a small quantity of their own dough.)

2   Give children a selection of packaging and let them fill them with a variety of dry materials - rice, different types of pasta, lentils, and so on. These can be used in the shop (see Unit 11).

3   Provide a selection of containers in the water/sand tray. Let the children practise pouring and filling. Ask them to find out how many cupfuls a jug or bottle will hold.

Plenary

Discuss activity 3. How many cups full of water/sand were held by the other containers? Which container holds the most? How did they work it out? Show the children a variety of containers with different amounts of water in. Ask the children to identify the empty containers and the full containers. If there are any that have water in but are not empty or full, ask the children to make them empty or full.

Money and real life problems

Unit 11

Objectives:

Count reliably up to ten objects

Recognise 1p coins

Solve practical problems involving counting in real life or role play

Sort and match objects

Vocabulary:

sort, coin, coins, money, pence, pennies, How much?, pay, buy, spend, customer, till, cost, bought

match, sort, How many?, more, enough, not enough, less, same, set

count, count out, number, one, two, three, four, five, six, seven, eight, nine, ten

References:

National Numeracy Strategy pages 2-8, 20-21

Curriculum Guidance for the Foundation Stage pages 68, 74-78

Session 1:

Resources:

Play food or pictures to represent five currant buns

Quantity of 1p coins (real or plastic); large, laminated, facsimile coins are useful for sticking on the board in whole class work (photocopiable sheet 25)

Blu-Tack (to stick coins on board)

Equipment for role-play shop - play food, price labels, till, money, purses, clothes for shopkeeper

Purses, containers or purse outlines

Price labels (up to 10p)

Pots or containers for sorting coins

Starter

Sing 'Five currant buns'. Choose one child to be the baker. Give five children a 1p coin each. Sing the song again and children pay one penny for each bun to the baker who gives them a bun in return (use play food or pictures). Stick the coin on the board. At the end of the song, ask the children how many coins are on the board. Count them. There are five. How much are they worth? Five pence.

Main teaching activity

In the home corner, set up a baker's shop. Put price labels on the items up to 10 pence. Ask the children to describe what happens when they go to the shops. Act out the role of the shopkeeper yourself first, selling the food, putting the money in the till. Then choose a child to be the shopkeeper (let him or her wear a hat, apron or label to identify their role). Choose another child to be a customer. Give the customer a purse containing 1 pence coins. Let the customer choose what to buy. Model the vocabulary: 'Can I have…?' 'How much does it cost?' Let the shopkeeper get the item. Ask the children how they know the cost of the item. Look at the price label.

Group activities

1   Give each child in the group a purse (or purse outline). Give each child a number of 1p coins. Ask them to count how much money they have. Then ask them to get a price label that matches the amount. When all the children have had a turn, ask the children to return all the coins to the centre of the table. Give each child a price label; each child says the price on their label and then gets the corresponding amount of 1p coins.

2   Explain that when money is taken to the bank, it needs to be counted into pots. You want the children to make sure that there are ten 1p coins in each pot. Count ten 1p coins into a pot to demonstrate. You may wish to put different amounts into the pots, so that the children have to empty the pot, count the amount and then ensure that 10p is put into the pot.

3   Let children play in the shop. All customers in the shop have 10p to spend.

Plenary

Ask the children to demonstrate activity 2. Ask children to show you what they have bought in the shop and respond to the question, 'How much did it cost?' Ask another child to count out the appropriate amount. Repeat.

Session 2:

Resources:

Play food buns and 1p coins (from session 1)

Real coins (1p, 2p, 5p, 10p) or large facsimiles (photocopiable sheet 25) and Blu-Tack

Purses, purse outlines or containers (as for session 1)

Quantity of 1p coins

Price labels (up to 10p)

Starter

Sing 'Five currant buns' using play food or pictures and 1p coins, as in session 1. Put all the buns on a table and price them all at 1p. Ask: 'If I buy two buns, how much do they cost altogether?' Repeat using different quantities up to and including five buns. Develop this theme by saying 'I have got 3 pence. How many buns can I buy?'

Main teaching activity

Show the children coins with the following values: 1p, 2p, 5p, 10p. Do they all look the same? Stick them on the board. Begin by discussing the shape of the coins. They are all circles. Look at the colours. Talk about the numbers that they can see.

Group activities

1   As for session 1.
2   Put out a selection of labels with amounts ranging from 1p to 10p inclusive. Give children purses/purse outlines or containers. Children count 1p coins to match the value indicated on the label they have chosen.
3   As for session 1.

Plenary

Discuss activity 2. Choose a purse or container from activity 2 and ask a child what they could buy from the shop for that amount. You may wish to extend the activity by asking what two things they could buy for that amount.

Session 3:

Resources:

Collection of classroom objects for sorting

Plastic set circles for sorting

Compare bears or other sorting animals

Snowmen outlines for children to colour (one per child)

Starter

Children sit in a circle and count together from one to 20. Begin to count around the circle from one to 20. Begin the count again, but when you get to three, stop. Restart the count at four on the other side of the circle. Stop the count at eight. Restart at a different point in the circle. (This activity encourages the children to retain a number and begin to count on.)

Main teaching activity

Put a variety of small objects in the centre, and position set circles on the floor. Ask a child to find all the crayons, for example, and put them into one circle, another child can put all the scissors in another circle, until all the items are sorted. Put them all back into the centre. Ask a child to find something red and put it into a circle. Ask another child to find a blue crayon and put it into another circle, and so on. Continue to sort according to colour.

Group activities

1   Put a variety of bears on the table. Ask the children to count out five bears each. Have three circles. Put a bear in each circle (different size). Tell the children that you are going to sort according to size. Take turns in putting a bear in a circle. When complete, return the bears to the centre. Change the sorting criteria to colour.
2   Children colour in snowmen outlines. Ask them to colour his hat green or blue, the scarf yellow or red. He has two buttons. See if children can sort the snowmen using their own criteria.
3   Provide extra items for the shop, and ask children to sort objects to go on different shelves, for example cakes, sandwiches, crisps, and so on.

Plenary

Use the snowmen from activity 2. Sort them into sets but do not tell the children the criteria you have used. Let them see if they can work it out, for example all red hats. Ask one child to sort the snowmen and the others guess the criteria. Ask the children to explain how they have reorganised the shop.

Session 4:

Resources:

Large numeral cards, washing line and pegs

Nine cubes per child

Bag containing pairs of objects, for example gloves, socks

Lotto, picture cards, numeral or dot cards (to play Pelmanism)

Paper and crayons

Starter

Children sit in circle. Display a set of numeral cards (zero to nine) on the washing line. Give each child nine cubes. Say a number, then point to it. Ask the children to get that amount of cubes and make a tower. How many cubes are in their tower? Is their tower the same size as the person's next to them? Get them to hold their towers up. Repeat using different numbers.

Main teaching activity

Explain that you have lots of things in your bag. They are all muddled up. Ask a child to take one item from the bag. Show the group. Another child then removes another object. Does it match? Take the objects one at a time from the bag, until all the objects are matched. Hold up a pair of items, for example gloves, to show how the design is the same on both hands.

Group activities

1   Play Pelmanism (pairs) using numeral cards (zero to nine) or dot cards. You may prefer to use ready-made pictures or pictorial lotto. The main objective is that the children find a matching object.

2   Children draw around their hands to make an outline for a pair of gloves. They can design their own patterns and colour them in.

3   Let the children have the bag of objects and match pairs. Introduce extra pairs of gloves and socks.

Plenary

Discuss activity 2. Choose a selection of the children's hand outlines and see if the children can sort them into pairs.

Session 5:

Resources:

Decide on a scenario – for a toy party, for example, you will need invitations with envelopes, plates, sandwiches, sweets, a selection of birthday cards (showing ages), goody bags, and candles

Paper/card and crayons for birthday card/banner

Starter

Sing 'One, two, buckle my shoe'. Recite the numbers from zero to ten and back, then from zero to 20.

Main teaching activity

Explain that today you are going to solve some problems. Create a scenario related directly to your children, for example a toy's party. How many toys are going to be at the party? Four toys have been asked. Show the children some invitations. 'How many do we need?' 'We need some envelopes as well.' Count them. 'I have only got three. How many more envelopes do I need? Yes, I need one more.' 'Teddy wants to bring a friend. Now how many are going to be at the party?' Five. Get six plates. All count them together. 'Have we got enough plates for each toy?' Yes. 'How many are left?' 'We have got one more plate than toys.' Match the plates to the toys (one to one correspondence).

Group activities

1   Working with an adult, build problems from the scenario. Put three sweets on the plate. 'Are there enough sweets for each toy to have one? No, we need to get some more. Let's work out how many more.' Get one more (don't put it on the plate). 'Have we got enough now? Let's count the sweets.' Repeat. 'Have we got enough now? Three on the plate and two more, that's five altogether.' All the toys like sandwiches. They all have one sandwich each (either cheese or jam). One toy has a jam sandwich. How many toys have cheese sandwiches?

2   The toys' party is to celebrate a fifth birthday. Children can design a birthday card/banner. Encourage the children to draw five objects, for example balloons.

3   Children set the table for five toys. Make sure each toy has one plate, one cup, and so on.

Plenary

Show the children a variety of birthday cards showing different ages. Ask: 'How old would someone be if they got this card?' Look at clues - the number of candles, numerals and so on. Count out six candles. 'Have I got enough candles for the toys' fifth party?' Get five toys. Set places for all of them. Let the children help. All the toys have a goody bag to take home. Make sure that one bag has only one item in. Is it fair? How can we make it fair? Discuss how they are going to solve the problem.

Assess and review

Unit 12

By the end of Unit 11, most children should be able to:

- Join in number rhymes
- Recite number names beyond ten (up to and including 20)
- Count reliably more than five objects (up to ten)
- Say one more/one less than a given number (up to and including ten)
- Use language - more or less, greater or smaller - to compare two numbers up to five and say which is more or less

- Recognise 1p coins
- Begin to solve practical problems involving counting in real life or role play
- Put sets of objects in order of size
- Sort and match objects
- Talk about and recognise simple symmetrical patterns
- Begin to use appropriate language to compare mass and capacity (heavy/light, full/empty)

- Name 2-d shapes (square, circle, rectangle, triangle)
- Begin to name 3-d shapes (cube, sphere, cylinder)

- Begin to use the vocabulary of time and sequence familiar events

- Begin to use everyday words to describe position (respond to the question 'Where is ...?' using vocabulary such as 'in', 'on', 'under', 'next to' and so on)

Remember that the information these assessments provide must be used to plan the children's activities at the appropriate level. This may mean revisiting, consolidating or extending the level at which the child is working.

Pages 13 to 15 of *Using Assess and Review Lessons* (DfES 0632/2001) provide examples of questions that can be used to assess a child's understanding against the key objectives.

Counting, comparing and ordering numbers

Unit 1

Objectives:

Say and use number names beyond ten in order in familiar contexts, for example number rhymes, songs, stories

Recite number names in order, continuing from two, three or four

Count reliably up to ten objects

Order a given set of numbers, for example one to six, given in random order

Vocabulary:

number, zero, one, two up to 20 and beyond

count, count up to, count in ones, starting at, starting from, back from

How many?, next, after, before, order, Which?

References:

National Numeracy Strategy pages 2-8, 11-13

Curriculum Guidance for the Foundation Stage pages 68, 74, 75

Session 1:

Resources:

Glove puppet (optional)
Large dot cards (zero to ten)
Set of dominoes
Containers with different numbers of items (for ordering)
Washing line
Sticky notes with numbers on

Starter

Children count up from zero to ten, then zero to 20. Continue the count up to 30. You can use a puppet for this activity if you wish. Tell the children that the puppet is (or you are) going to count up to ten, but they need to listen very carefully as he (or you) may miss out a number. If they hear a mistake they must put their thumbs up, then you will ask a child to identify the mistake. Repeat the activity. Extend the numbers used up to 20.

Main teaching activity

Give out large dot cards zero to ten to different children. Who has zero? Bring the card to the front of the class. What number should come next? Continue until the card showing ten dots is reached. As you say the number, ask the child to hold up their card.

Group activities

1   The aim is to order the dominoes according to value. Place a set of dominoes face down. You turn one over and a child turns one over. Which is more/the largest number? Ask another child to turn over a domino. Count the spots. Continue the process, discussing where to place the domino. (Put matching values on top of each other.)

2   Children order a collection of objects in containers, smallest number to largest.

3   Children order the large dot cards on the washing line.

Plenary

Look at the washing line. Show children some sticky notes with numbers on.
Can they help you to put them on the correct dot card?

Session 2:

Resources:
Large numeral cards (zero to ten) and washing line
Large dot cards
Containers labelled with one to six dots; cubes
Ladybird cards and dominoes with one to six dots

Starter

Put the numeral cards on the floor in random order. Count together from zero to ten. Ask a child to find zero. Attach it to the washing line. What number will come next? Continue up to ten.

Main teaching activity

Put the large dot cards on the washing line in the wrong order. Count from zero to ten, pointing to the cards. Does the number said match the amount shown? No. Can they tell you which numbers are in the wrong place?

Group activities

1   Give each child a large dot card. Put the remainder on the washing line in the correct order, leaving spaces. Ask a child to say how many dots are on their card. Can they work out where to put the missing card? What number comes before four? Three. Can they find that on the line? Repeat.

2   Children order the numbered containers and put in the corresponding amount of cubes. Children mix up the containers. Can another child put them back in the correct order?

3   Hide around the classroom some ladybird cards with one to six spots on and dominoes with one to six dots. Children find them and arrange them in order.

Plenary

Use the containers from activity 2. Mix them up. How many cubes should be in this container? Look at the label. Ask a child to check the amount by counting the cubes. Put them in front of the container. Repeat until all containers are empty. Ask them to order the cubes starting at one.

Session 3:

Resources:
Counting Rhymes by John Foster (Oxford University Press)
'Ten in the bed' (photocopiable sheet 15)
Cubes of the same colour
A variety of sorting objects (buttons, cubes)
Large dot cards and washing line
Ladybird cards and dominoes (as for session 2)
Paper and pencils

Starter

Say 'One, two, three, four' from *Counting Rhymes*. Using fingers, count up to ten. Say a number and children hold up the corresponding number of fingers. ('Show me', as in Autumn Unit 1, session 5.) 'How many fingers have you got? Let's count them … one, two, three, four ….'

Main teaching activity

Use the 'Ten in the bed' photocopiable resource. Count how many teddies are in the bed. Then, using a variety of sorting objects, ask the children to count out how many buttons, cubes, and so on, there are, up to ten in value.

Group activities

1   As for session 2.

2   Children make towers of ten cubes using the same colour.

3   As for session 2.

Plenary

Count with children the number of cubes in the towers. Are they the same size? How many are there? Show the children the dot cards from one to six. See if they can order them. 'Which card is first?' One. 'What will come next?' Let a child find the card. Continue until all six are in order. 'What will come next?' Seven. Ask a child to draw spots to make a dot card for number seven.

Session 4:

Resources:
Ten objects in a bag
Puppet (as for session 1)
2 x 5 grids (enough for each child)
A die labelled 0, 1, 1, 2, 2, 3
Counters
Towers of up to ten cubes
Containers labelled with dots and numerals up to ten
Bears, buttons and sand tray

Starter
Children sit in a circle. Starting at zero, all count to 20. Count again, but this time around the circle. Stop. Next time, begin the count at one and count around the circle up to ten. Stop. Begin the count at two and count around the circle, stopping at ten. Repeat the activity, beginning the count at three and four.

Main teaching activity
Using a selection of ten objects in a bag, count them out one at a time. When all ten objects are out of the bag, reintroduce the puppet. Let the puppet count them, but make sure he does not attach one number name to each object. Ask the children if he is right. Get children to demonstrate how to count by touching and moving the objects. Let the puppet attempt to count the objects. He is unsure of numbers beyond five, so the children will have to help him.

Group activities
1   Give each child a 2 x 5 grid. Children take it in turns to roll the die and take the corresponding number of counters. When they place them on the grid, count how many counters they have. The first child to collect ten counters wins.

2   Explain that the puppet has made towers of cubes and put them into labelled containers but he is still making mistakes. (Differentiate by using smaller amounts.) The children need to take out the towers, count the cubes and put them into the correct containers.

3   Bury ten buttons and ten bears in the sand. Children have to find all the objects. Some children may need a dot card to match the object to.

Plenary
Discuss activities 2 and 3. Let a child count the cubes in the tower. Now can the puppet do it correctly?

Session 5:

Resources:
Large numeral cards (zero to ten) and washing line
Dominoes
Puppet (as for session 1)
Cubes
Dot cards
A die
Buttons and bears for sand tray

Starter
Before the session, put the numerals zero to ten on the washing line. Say the rhyme 'One, two, buckle my shoe'. Give children one domino each (up to a total of ten dots). Ask the children to count the number of dots on their domino. Point to the numerals as you say them in order. Pause after each number and ask the children that have that amount of dots to hold their domino in the air.

Main teaching activity
Explain that today your puppet is going to count out some cubes. Ask the children to choose a dot card. Ask how many dots are on the card, for example six. Can the puppet get six cubes? Hesitate when you get to five. 'How many cubes did he have to get?' Six. 'Has he got enough?' No. Carry on until he has got six. Repeat using other numbers - make sure numbers nine and ten are used.

Group activities
1   Give each child a dot card with either nine or ten dots. Put the dominoes face down on the table. Children take turns to choose a domino. If the total of spots is the same as that on their card the child keeps the domino.

2   Children roll a die and take the corresponding number of cubes. The first child to get a total of ten wins.

3   As for session 4.

Plenary
Count up to ten using fingers. Ask a child to count out ten cubes. Begin to count out ten cubes. Pause when you get to four. Can the children continue to count as you get more cubes? Can they stop or tell you to stop when you get to ten?

Counting, adding and subtracting

Unit 2

Objectives:

Count reliably up to 12 objects

Begin to use the language involved in adding

Begin to relate addition to combining two groups of objects, counting all objects

Separate (partition) a given number of objects into two groups

Vocabulary:

add, more, and, make, total, altogether, one more, count all, groups, same

How many?, count, number names up to 20

separate, imagine

References:

National Numeracy Strategy pages 2-8, 14-17

Curriculum Guidance for the Foundation Stage pages 68, 69, 74-77

Session 1:

Resources:

Large numeral cards, washing line and dominoes

Counters, cubes and a die

Two sets of dot cards (one to five), paper and pencils (for activity 2)

Set of dot cards (for activity 3)

Starter

Put numeral cards zero to ten on the washing line. Give children one domino each (up to a total of ten dots). Ask them to count the number of dots on the domino. Point to the numbers as you say them in order. Pause after each number and ask the children with that amount of dots to hold up their domino. Point to numbers at random. Say the number and children hold up the domino with the corresponding number of dots.

Main teaching activity

Get two girls to stand at the front of the classroom. Ask: 'How many girls can you see?' Two. Now get three boys to stand up. 'How many boys are there?' Three. 'How many girls and boys are there altogether?' As you ask this question, move the two groups together. Count them all. Repeat the process using four girls and two boys.

Group activities

1   Children take turns in rolling a die. They take a corresponding amount of counters. Roll the die again. Take the corresponding amount of cubes. Count each group then count how many there are altogether.

2   Put two sets of dot cards face down. Children take turns to turn over two cards. Count how many dots altogether. Draw that number of dots on a separate piece of paper.

3   Children draw two sweet jars (or circles to represent jars). Let them pick two dot cards. They count the dots on each card and draw the corresponding amount of sweets in the jars. Count how many sweets altogether.

Plenary

Discuss activities 2 and 3.

Session 2:

Resources:

As for session 1, plus puppet (optional)

Starter

Children count from zero to ten, then zero to 20 (using a puppet if you wish). Tell the children that you are going to count up to ten, but they need to listen carefully as you may miss out a number. When they hear a mistake they must put their thumbs up. Ask a child to identify the mistake. Repeat the activity. Extend the numbers used up to 20.

Main teaching/group activities

As for session 1, but change the objects used to combine and ask the children to draw birds' nests instead of sweet jars.

Plenary

Discuss activities 2 and 3.

Session 3:

Resources:

Cubes and strip of card

Straws and pictures or objects to partition, for example pasta shapes

Ladybird outlines and six spots per child

Paper plates and play food (cardboard biscuits)

Starter

Play 'Shaking fingers', a variation on 'Show me'. Children shake their fingers in front of them then fold their arms, hiding their fingers under their armpits. Say: 'Show me four fingers!' Children hold up their fingers. This gives you an opportunity to watch and assess the children's responses as hiding their fingers before showing you prevents children copying. Children shake their fingers and hide them. Repeat using any number between one and ten.

Main teaching activity

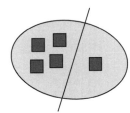

Ask a child to count out five cubes. Use a strip of card to partition the set. Use the board and draw what you have done for everyone to see. Ask 'How many cubes are there on this side of the set?' Four. Write the number four under the group. Repeat, recording one. Remove the strip of card. Ask: 'How many cubes are there altogether?' Say: 'Four and one makes five'. Repeat the process, moving the strip of card.

Group activities

1   Use an outline of a ladybird and six spots.
    The children arrange the spots on the ladybird while you (or an adult) scribe number sentences, for example
    $1 + 5 = 6, 2 + 4 = 6$

2   Give children paper plates and let them investigate different ways of putting seven 'biscuits' on to the plate.

3   Print or stick five objects onto paper. Use a straw to partition the objects. Stick the straw onto the paper.

Plenary

Discuss activity 3. Count how many objects are on the paper altogether. Count how many are on one side of the straw. How many are on the other side of the straw? (For example, three and two makes five.) You can scribe the numbers.

Session 4:

Resources:

As for session 3

Starter

Sing 'One potato, two potato, three potato, four'. Imagining is an important skill for the children to develop. Ask them to close their eyes and ask: 'Can you see two lollipops?' 'A friend gives you one more. How many lollipops can you see now?' 'Open your eyes. Hold up your fingers to show the answer.' 'Close your eyes. Think about a plate with three cakes on it. A friend gives you one more. Count the cakes that are on the plate now. Open your eyes, hold up your fingers and show me the answer.'

Main teaching/group activities

As for session 3 but increase the amount of cubes to partition. Use up to ten cubes, biscuits, and so on.

Plenary

Count out ten sweets/biscuits. 'How many biscuits are there?' Ten. Put all ten on one plate. Move one. Count how many are on one plate: nine and one on the other. 'How many altogether?' Continue moving one. Can the children begin to predict the pattern?

Session 5:

Resources:

Sponge cake mix (or ingredients to make a cake)

Patty/cake tin (with 12 spaces)

Beads and laces, playdough, egg boxes

Starter

Sing 'One, two, three, four, five, once I caught a fish alive'.

Whole class activity

Play 'Show me'. 'Show me five fingers!' Fold one finger down. 'How many fingers are up now?' Four. 'How many are down?' One. 'How many fingers altogether?' Five. 'Fold down two. How many are up?' Three. 'How many fingers altogether?' Five. Continue.

Group activities

1   Make up a simple sponge cake recipe. Take a cake tin with 12 spaces. Ask: 'How many cakes can we put in this tray?' Count the empty spaces. Get children to count out 12 cake cases. Count as the children put the cases into the tin. Count as the mixture is put into the cases.

2   Make necklaces, all 12 beads long.

3   Using playdough, children make egg shapes or cakes to go into cake containers or egg boxes.

Plenary

Begin to discuss activity 3. 'How many eggs have you made?' Take them out of the boxes and ask children to count them. Count how many compartments there are. Twelve. Count them into the boxes. When nine are in place, count the empty spaces. 'How many more do I need?' Three. Put another one in. 'How many eggs are in the boxes?' Ten. 'How many more do I need?' Repeat. Discuss and count the beads in the necklaces.

Enjoy the cakes at the end of the day!

Shape, space and reasoning

Unit 3

Objectives:

Begin to name solids and flat shapes

Use shapes to describe and make models, pictures, patterns

Solve simple problems or puzzles in a practical context

Match objects (shapes)

Sort and match objects, shapes or pictures, justifying the decisions made

Vocabulary:

straight, curved, sides, corners, same, long, short, match, length

2-d shapes, square, circle, triangle, rectangle, flat, shape

count, number names up to 30

repeating pattern, What will come next?, before, after, arrange

References:

National Numeracy Strategy pages 18-19, 24-27

Curriculum Guidance for the Foundation Stage pages 69, 78-81

Note: You may find it useful to take photographs of patterns in your environment.

Session 1:

Resources:

Selection of 2-d shapes, to include at least 12 straight-sided shapes

Die numbered 1, 1, 3, 3, 4, 4

Shape lotto (photocopiable sheets 10-12)

Starter

Give each child a 2-d shape. Keep a selection of large shapes yourself. Ask the children: 'Hold up your shape if it's a square/if it's a circle', and so on. Begin to extend your questioning: 'Hold up your shape if it has three sides/four sides the same length/straight sides', and so on. Ask children to stand up if they have straight-sided shapes. Collect in 12, counting aloud. Keep these to one side for the plenary.

Main teaching activity

Sing 'Wind the bobbin' (traditional). Focus on the phrase 'Point to the window'. What shape is the window? 'Point to the door.' What shape is the door? Play 'I spy': 'I spy with my little eye a square shape'. Ask the children to look around the class for different square shapes. Repeat using different shapes.

Group activities

1   Play shape lotto. Roll the die. If the children have a shape with the same number of sides they cover that shape.

2   Using plastic shapes as a reference point, children look around the immediate area to find similar shapes in the environment.

3   Children look for shapes around the classroom and record by drawing, for example a clock (circle), a table (rectangle).

Plenary

Count all 12 straight-sided shapes. Can the children suggest different criteria to sort the shapes? (number of sides/corners/sides the same length and so on)

Session 2:

Resources:

Pictures of patterns or patterned wrapping paper/clothing

Selection of 2-d shapes and washing line

Paper or card circles and squares in two different colours

Strips of paper, glue

Pattern cards (patterns for children to copy) and cubes

Starter

Count from zero to 20. Can anyone say what number comes after 20? Begin to expose the children to the numbers beyond 20. Just go to 30. Once the children grasp the idea that it is 21, 22, 23, and so on, they will find counting beyond comparatively easy. Ask children to play 'Show me', as in Unit 1, session 5.

Explain that today you are going to look at repeating patterns. Look at some pictures/wrapping paper/clothing. Discuss the patterns they can see, for example stripes on a zebra crossing.

Main teaching activity

Choose two shapes, for example circles and squares. Use the washing line. Ask a child to choose one shape, for example a circle, and attach it to the line. Then add a square, then a circle. Can the children predict what shape will come next? Keep adding shapes until there are 12 shapes on the line.

Group activities

1   Put out some circles and squares in two different colours. Ask the children to choose a square, then a circle in a different colour. Choose another. Discuss what they think will come next in their patterns. Stick their patterns onto strips of paper.

2   Let children choose a pattern card and copy the pattern using cubes.

3   Children choose two shapes and on a long strip of paper print a repeating pattern.

Plenary

Discuss the patterns made in activities 1 and 3.

Session 3:

Resources:

Selection of 2-d shapes

Large wax crayons and paper

Camera (optional)

Selection of different coloured beads

Pre-cut paper shapes

Starter

Play a simple 'copy and clap' action game, for example, touch your nose, clap, touch your nose, then clap. Can the children continue the pattern? Tap your head, clap twice, repeat. Gradually make the actions more complex.

Main teaching activity

Choose three shapes. Can the children name the shapes? Arrange them in a repeating pattern, for example square, circle, triangle, square. Can the children predict what will come next? Try an arrangement of two squares, one triangle, one circle.

Group activities

1   Take children on a walk around the area. Using large wax crayons, make rubbings of repeating patterns. (A camera may be useful to record patterns that are found.)

2   Give children a selection of beads to make repeating patterns using just two colours.

3   Give the children the beginning of a pattern using 2-d shapes or pre-cut paper shapes. Can they continue the pattern?

Plenary

Use shapes of two different sizes and arrange them: one large square, one circle, one small square, one large square, one circle. What shape will come next? Discuss today's activities.

Session 4:

Resources:
Tom Thumb's Musical Maths (A & C Black)
Selection of 2-d and 3-d shapes
Pictures from catalogues and magazines to sort

Starter

Sing 'Which shapes?' from *Tom Thumb's Musical Maths*. Play a simple game whereby you give each child a shape (it can be 2-d or 3-d). Ask the children to look at their shape. Choose a child to stand up. Ask the other children to look carefully at their shape. Has another child got the same shape? Can they name their shape or key features of it, for example 'It is 3-d', 'It will roll', and so on.

Main teaching activity

Children sit in a circle. Put an assortment of 2-d and 3-d shapes in the middle of the group. Ask a child to sort them and say how they have sorted them. Encourage them to justify their choices. Let another child sort according to their own criteria. Some children may sort according to colour, straight or curved, 2-d or 3-d.

Group activities

1   Children sort different shapes and explain their criteria.

2   Children make patterns or pictures using 2-d and/or 3-d shapes.

3   Give the children a selection of pictures from catalogues and magazines for them to sort into sets.

Plenary

Discuss activities 2 and 3.

Session 5:

Resources:
Rectangular pieces of paper (to represent packed lunch boxes)
Circular pieces of paper (school dinners)
Square pieces of paper (home dinners)
Dolls' house and furniture
Animal pictures

Starter

Sit children in a circle. Count up to 20 together. Count around the circle. Say a number less than ten. What number comes before/after it?

Main teaching activity

Count how many children are in the class. Sort the children into groups: Who has long/short hair? Who has brown eyes? and so on

Group activities

1   Children choose appropriate shaped pieces of paper and draw sandwiches, a school dinner or a home dinner. Discuss how many children within the group have packed lunches. Do more children go home for dinner?

2   Put all the dolls' house furniture in a box. Can the children sort the items into the appropriate rooms?

3   Give the children a selection of animal pictures to sort, for example according to number of legs, whether they can fly, and so on

Plenary

Discuss activity 1. How many children have packed lunches? How many children go home for dinner? How many children have school dinners? Make a display by arranging the pictures in three separate circles. Write the total amounts of each group. Are there more children going home or having school dinners? Discuss activities 2 and 3.

Counting and measures

Objectives:

Recite the number names in order, counting back from six, five or four

Use language such as 'more' or 'less', 'longer' or 'shorter', 'heavier' or 'lighter' (length, mass, time) to make direct comparisons of two quantities

Vocabulary:

count, count up to, numbers zero to 30, fold down, count back from

more, most, least, less, container, funnel, full, empty, almost, fill, pour

more than, less than, the same

long, longer than, short, shorter than, the same length

days of the week, Sunday, Monday, Tuesday, Wednesday, Thursday, Friday, Saturday

before, after, today, tomorrow, yesterday

References:

National Numeracy Strategy pages 2-8, 22-23

Curriculum Guidance for the Foundation Stage pages 69-70, 74-75, 80-81

Session 1:

Resources:

Large dot cards
Set of dot cards per child (for activity 1)
Set of dominoes and pieces of paper divided into three
Resources for drawing/printing, playdough

Starter

Count around the circle up to ten. Count around the circle up to 20, then 30. Explain that now you are going to count back from five. 'Hold up five fingers. Fold one down - four, fold one down – three …' Continue until you get to zero. Repeat, reminding the children to fold down their fingers.

Main teaching activity

Recap on the vocabulary 'more' and 'less'. Display the large dot cards. Ask the children to find a card with six dots. 'Find a card with one more dot. One more than six is how many?' 'Two more than six is … ?' Continue using different starting points. Ask 'What is one less than….?' Repeat the questions using different starting points.

Group activities

1   Give the children a set of dot cards each up to ten. Ask questions such as 'Show me a number more than six'. Children explain their choice and then turn the card over. 'Show me a number less than two.' The winner is the first child to have turned over all their cards.

2   Give each child a domino and a piece of paper divided into three. They count all the spots on the domino and draw the same number in the middle section. They complete by drawing one less dot and one more dot, for example:

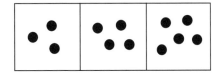

3   Children make two sets which contain the same amount by drawing, printing, using dough.

Plenary

Count back from five.

Session 2:

Resources:

Five plastic containers and a jug of water

Four plastic bottles (all the same size) and a funnel

A set of plastic beakers and a jug of drinking water/squash

Access to the sand or water tray

Starter

Sing 'Ten green bottles'. Count up to ten. Stop. Remind everyone that yesterday you counted back from five, using your fingers to help you. 'Hold up five fingers. Let's start at number five and count back' (folding down fingers as before). Then point to the number five on the number line and count back to zero. Next time start at number six and count back.

Main teaching activity

Count out five plastic containers. Put different amounts of water into four of them. (Make sure that one is full.) Ask the children which ones are empty and which are full. 'How can I make this container empty?' Take a container that is not full. 'How can I make this container full?'

Group activities

1 Show the children four plastic bottles (all the same size). Show the children a funnel and how it works. Can they put different amounts of liquid into each bottle? Arrange the bottles in order. Is there a container that is empty or nearly empty, full or nearly full? Ask children: 'Has this container got more liquid in than this one?' 'Which container has got the most/least?'

2 Give the children a set of plastic beakers. Can they fill each beaker to the same level with water/squash? (drinks for the children) They all need the same amount.

3 Children play in the sand or water tray. Can they put water/sand into containers so they are half full?

Plenary

Ask the children whether they found it difficult to put the same amount of drink into each beaker. How did they do it? Discuss activity 3. If they are all half full, is there the same amount in each container? Are all the containers the same size?

Session 3:

Resources:

Selection of ribbons (different widths and lengths) – two of each kind

Straws cut to different lengths

Cubes

Beads and laces for necklaces

Playdough

Starter

Count up to 20. Start at number three and let the children continue the count. Say: 'Now we are going to count back from ten together.' Can individual children count back from six?

Main teaching activity

Display a selection of ribbons. Give each child a straw or a ribbon. Hold up a ribbon yourself. 'Has anyone got a straw the same length as this?' 'Look at the ribbons. Which is the longest ribbon?' 'Which is the shortest ribbon?' 'Hold up your ribbon or straw if it is shorter than this ribbon.' Ask a child how you can find out if it is shorter/longer, and so on.

Group activities

1 Make a line of cubes. Ask the children to make a line of cubes that is longer/shorter than yours. Compare the lines within the group. Who has got the longest line? Is Joshua's longer than Grace's?

2 Children make a long and short necklace.

3 Make a playdough snake. Children make a snake that is longer and one that is shorter.

Plenary

Order according to length the ribbons used at the beginning of the lesson. Use some of the necklaces from activity 2 and see who has made the longest necklaces. Discuss activity 3.

Session 4:

Resources:
Jasper's Beanstalk Mick Inkpen (Hodder Children's Books)
Picture prompts from the book
Paper and crayons
Jigsaws or sequencing cards

Starter
Read *Jasper's Beanstalk*.

Main teaching activity
Ask children to recite the days of the week. Children may know the names but not necessarily the correct order. Can they tell you what happened in the story? Encourage them to try and remember what happened on what day. Pictures drawn from the book will act as useful prompts.

Group activities
1   Ask children to draw a picture relating to the story. What day did Jasper do this? You can act as scribe and write the appropriate day.
2   Children use jigsaws, sequencing cards or pictures to sequence the events.
3   Let the children draw three or four pictures related to their day, and then sequence them.

Plenary
Ask children to talk about the pictures related to their day and how they have sequenced them. Read the story of *Jasper's Beanstalk* again but this time substitute the children's pictures.

Session 5:

Resources:
Harlequin (A & C Black)
Large sheet of paper for chart
Small versions of weather chart for group activity
Pictures, jigsaws and sequencing cards
Card for weather chart
Paper and crayons

Starter
Sing 'Each day different' (from *Harlequin*).

Main teaching activity
Recite the days of the week in order, starting with Sunday, then repeat. Start on Tuesday or Wednesday. Ask questions: 'What day is it today?' 'What day was it yesterday?' 'What will tomorrow be?' 'What day comes before/after Sunday?' Count how many days are in one week. 'What days do we come to school?'

Take a large sheet of paper and divide it into three sections: yesterday, today, tomorrow. Add the days, as appropriate.

yesterday	today	tomorrow
Thursday	Friday	Saturday

Ask questions: 'What did we do yesterday?' Record in pictures: 'What was the weather like yesterday?' 'What is the weather like today?' 'Do we know what the weather will be like tomorrow?'

Group activities
1   All children have a smaller version of the above sheet and draw appropriate pictures.
2   Children use sequencing cards, pictures or jigsaws to sequence events.
3   As for session 4.

Plenary
Recite the days of the week several times. Tell the children that next week they are going to record the weather on a large chart. They will have to mark the chart two times every day when the register is called. Label the chart with the days of the week. Children can remind you of the order as you write them onto the chart. Label 'morning' and 'afternoon'.

Counting, adding and subtracting

Unit 5

Session 1:

Resources:

Large dot cards and sticky notes showing numerals up to ten

Washing line

Board games (snakes and ladders, ludo)

Two dice

Toy farm animals

Starter

Count up to ten together, then count up to 20. Use large dot cards with sticky notes attached showing numerals up to ten. Place them on the floor randomly. Children attach them to the washing line in the correct order. Children close their eyes while you change two cards around. Children open their eyes. Can they find the mistakes? Repeat.

Main teaching activity

Explain that you are going to look at different ways of making the same total. Ask six children to come to the front of the group (all stand to your right). Count the children. Say: 'There are six children on this side. How many are on the other side?' None. 'Move one child over to your left. 'Count how many are on my left. There are five. How many are on the other side? One. Five and one more makes six altogether.' Repeat using the same phrases until all six children are on your left-hand side.

Group activities

1   Play a simple board game, such as snakes and ladders or ludo.
2   Throw two dice. Find different ways of making nine.
3   Let children have ten objects, for example toy farm animals. How many different ways can they put them into two different fields (one and nine, two and eight, and so on).

Plenary

Children can share their different findings about ways of making nine and ten.

Session 2:

Resources:

A drum

Ten objects for counting (pictures of lollipops, cakes and so on)

Die (labelled 1, 1, 2, 2, 3, 3 in numerals or dots)

Ten counters per child

Cubes or pegboard

Objects to hide in the sand tray

Starter

Ask children to listen carefully as you hit a drum. Explain that you want them to count how many times you hit it. Start with a small number. Ask a child to come and hit the drum six times while the class counts. Increase the number up to 12.

Main teaching activity

Count out five objects. (I find pictures of edible objects useful.) 'How many lollipops have I got?' Five. 'I am going to take one lollipop away. How many lollipops have I got left? Let's count them. There are four. If I take two lollipops away, how many have I got left? Let's count them. There are one, two.' Next time take two away so there are no lollipops left. Count out ten objects and repeat the process, asking the children to take away one, two, three or four objects.

Group activities

1   Give every child ten counters. They take it in turns to throw the die. The number thrown shows how many counters they have to take away. The aim is to reduce the number of counters to zero. They must throw an exact amount at the end. The child who manages to get rid of all their counters is the winner.

2   Using cubes or a pegboard, make a staircase pattern descending in steps of two.

3   Children can create subtraction problems using the sand tray. They start with five objects. They hide …. in the sand. How many are left?

Plenary

Discuss activities 2 and 3.

Session 3:

Resources:

Large dot cards and washing line; sticky notes showing numerals to ten

One die (labelled with 1, 2, 3, 4, 5, 6 spots), one die (labelled with 1, 1, 2, 2, 3, 3 spots)

Cubes

Board games such as snakes and ladders

Objects to hide in the sand tray

Large number track (zero to ten) (photocopiable sheet 7)

Large die (labelled 1, 1, 2, 2, 3, 3)

Starter

Sing 'Ten green bottles'.

Main teaching activity

Put all ten dot cards in order on the washing line, starting at ten and counting back. Put sticky notes showing numerals on each card. Count back from ten. Ask questions such as 'What is one less than …?'

Group activities

1   Children roll the first die and pick up cubes to the value of one to six. They then roll the second die and take away one, two or three cubes, depending on the number thrown. Count how many cubes are left.

2   Play simple board games, such as snakes and ladders.

3   As for session 2.

Plenary

Sing 'Ten in the bed'. Use a large number track up to ten. Put a marker on number ten. Roll the large die (numbered 1, 1, 2, 2, 3, 3). Move the counter back the appropriate number of spaces until zero is reached.

Session 4:

Resources:

Selection of coins (1p, 2p, 5p)

Blu-Tack

Purse outlines for each child

Wax crayons and paper for rubbings

Quantity of 1p coins (for use in shop)

Items from the role-play shop (with price labels)

Play food to represent currant buns

Starter

Sing 'Five currant buns'. Count up to ten saying one pence, two pence, three pence … Point to the appropriate coin. Highlight that there aren't coins for 3p, 4p and so on.

Main teaching activity

Children sit in a circle. Put a selection of 1p, 2p and 5p coins in the middle of the class. 'When you went to the baker's shop, you bought a currant bun. How much did the bun cost?' One pence. Hold up a 1p coin. Stick five 1p coins to the board. Count them. Identify the other coins as 2p and 5p.

Group activities

1   Give each child a selection of coins. Ask them to hold up the same coin as you are holding. 'How much is it worth?' Then ask the children to find a 1p coin. Can they find 2p and 5p coins? Can the children give you two pennies, a 5 pence piece, and so on?

2   Give children a purse outline each and a pot of 1p coins. Give them a total of coins to put in the purse by doing wax crayon rubbings (differentiate groups by total).

3   Children use 1p coins to buy items from the shop.

Plenary

Count how much is in each purse. Children show items that they have paid for in the shop. Look at the price label. 'How much does this cost?' Ask another child to count out the correct amount of 1p coins. Sing 'Five currant buns'. Give five children 1p each. Display the buns for each child to buy. As each penny is paid, attach it to the board. At the end, count how many 1ps are on the board. Five. Model the sentence: 'There are five 1p coins. How much is that worth? Five pence.'

Session 5:

Resources:
Quantity of coins (1p, 2p, 5p)
Mail order catalogue
Price labels (1p, 2p, 5p) and Blu-Tack
A 1p rubber stamp
'Collect the 1p coin' game (photocopiable sheet 26)
Sorting tray
Die labelled 0, 1, 1, 2, 2, 0

Starter

Give each child a coin. Hold up a 1p coin. 'This is a one penny. If you have a one penny coin, hold it up in the air.' Repeat with the two pence and five pence coins. Then ask the children to hold up a coin worth two pence. You then hold your coin up so that the children can match theirs. Repeat with other coins. Order the coins according to value. Emphasise that there are no 3p or 4p coins.

Main teaching activity

Show the children a catalogue. Look at the types of things that you can buy. Tell them that you are going to make a catalogue for a jumble sale. (This allows the prices to be in small amounts.) Show the children pictures of items you are going to put in the catalogue. Show them the price labels. Read the price: 'Two pence. How many 1p coins do I need?' Ask the children to get the correct amount of coins and stick them with Blu-Tack to the label.

Group activities

1   Play the 'Collect the 1p coin' game. Use 1p coins. Roll the die and collect the appropriate amount of 1p coins. The first person to collect ten pennies wins the game.

2   Sort coins by value/colour.

3   Children use a rubber stamp to stamp 1p coins onto price labels for the catalogue.

Plenary

Look at the coins (activity 2). Have they been sorted correctly? 'How much is this coin worth?' Take the labels with coins stamped onto them. Count how many 1p coins there are. 'What price do I need to write on the label?' Attach labels to items in the catalogue. Ask questions about how much the book costs, and so on.

Assess and review

Unit 6

During the spring term, Units 1 to 5, children have built upon skills introduced during the autumn term. It is important to remember that some children may be experiencing initial difficulties and that work should be differentiated. Other children will need to be challenged. Make sure that your assessments reflect what you have actually taught and what experiences the children have had during this term.

By the end of Unit 5, most children should be able to:

■ Say and use number names in familiar contexts beyond ten
■ Recite number names up to 20, and beyond
■ Recite number names in descending order from ten (extend if appropriate)
■ Recite number names in order, continuing from two, three or four
■ Recite number names in order counting back from six, five or four
■ Say what number comes before/after any number less than ten
■ Order a given set of numbers (one to six) when given in random order
■ Count a collection of up to 12 objects (note whether they have a method for ensuring that all objects are counted only once)
■ Begin to use language related to adding
■ Begin to relate addition to combining two groups and counting all; say how many there are altogether
■ Partition a given number of objects into two groups
■ Begin to use language involved in subtracting
■ Begin to relate subtraction to taking away, and counting how many are left

■ Recognise coins: 1p, 2p, 5p
■ Sort coins by value
■ Use coins to pay for things

■ Begin to recite the days of the week

■ Identify 2-d shapes
■ Identify 3-d shapes
■ Use appropriate language to describe shape (curved, straight, edge, corner, flat, does and doesn't roll)

Remember that the information these assessments provide must be used to plan the children's activities at the appropriate level. This may mean revisiting, consolidating or extending the level at which the child is working.

Pages 13 to 15 of *Using Assess and Review Lessons* (DfES 0632/2001) provide examples of questions that can be used to assess a child's understanding against the key objectives.

Counting, comparing and ordering numbers

Unit 7

Objectives:

Say and use number names up to 20 in order in familiar contexts, for example rhymes, songs, stories

Recognise numerals one to three

Compare two numbers

Say a number that lies between two given numbers up to ten (then beyond)

Vocabulary:

number, zero to 20 and beyond, count, count up to, back from

How many?, next, before, after, same, match

compare, between, missing

most, least, more than, less than, order, bigger/larger, smaller, middle

References:

National Numeracy Strategy pages 2-9, 11-13

Curriculum Guidance for the Foundation Stage pages 68, 74-75

Session 1:

Resources:

Glove puppet

12 counting objects

Labels 'more than' and 'less than'

Plastic wallets containing different amounts of objects/pictures/counters

Sorting trays with numeral cards one, two, and three and sorting objects

Towers of cubes and pieces of paper divided into three

Paper and paint for printing

Starter

Count up to 20, then up to 30. Introduce the puppet. Explain that he (or she) is learning how to count up to 20 and that he wants to show the children what he can do. As he counts, he misses out numbers. Let the children tell the puppet about his mistakes. Let him say 'nineteen', for example, then pause. Can they say the next number?

Main teaching activity

Put ten counting objects on the floor. As you point to each object and move it, the children can say the number. Put all ten back together. Get another set of items, this time containing 12, and count them. Which set has the most/least? Get children to make sets of more than ten and less than ten objects. Ask the children to help you count how many objects there are. Label 'less than ten' and 'more than ten'.

Group activities

1   Give children a set of plastic wallets containing different amounts of objects (differentiate as appropriate). Let the children count them. Make sure that they give each item a number when they count. Write a label to show how many there are. Ask the children 'Who has the most?' 'Who has the least?' 'Has anyone got more than _____?' 'Has anyone got less than_____ ?'

2   Put numeral cards one, two and three in the bottom of three sorting trays (you may differentiate by increasing the value on the numeral cards). Ask children to put the corresponding number of items into the trays.

3   Give the children a tower of cubes and a piece of paper divided into three. Children count the number of cubes and print the same number of thumb prints in the middle section. Print more and less in the remaining two sections.

Plenary

Discuss all the activities. Focus on activity 3. Children count how many prints are in the two outer sections. Can they guess what the middle number might be?

Session 2:

Resources:

Die

Dot cards and Blu-Tack

Number lotto (3 x 2 grid) with numerals written in (make sure that each card is different)

Counters

Numeral cards (photocopiable sheets 3-6 or commercially produced cards)

Cards or pictures showing numbers for children to look for on a number hunt

Starter

Children sit in a circle. Count up to 20 together. Starting at zero, begin to count around the circle. Stop at five. Can the children work out who will say number seven? Start at seven and continue counting. Stop the children and ask them to work out who will say other numbers. Now play a game where you all take it in turns to roll the die, say how many dots you can see and then count up to ten.

Main teaching activity

Show the children the dot cards for one, two, three, four and five. Put the cards on the board. Count the dots. Explain that instead of having to count all the dots you can write numbers instead. Write the numbers alongside the cards. Remove the dot cards. Shuffle them. Can the children match the dot cards to the numbers?

Group activities

1   Play number lotto using a 3 x 2 grid with numbers written on (make sure that every card is different). (If children can recognise beyond the number three the numbers on the cards should reflect this.) Hold up a numeral card. Ask: 'Who has got this number?' 'What is this number?' Children put a counter over the number. The first child to cover all six squares wins the game.

2   Play Pelmanism (pairs). Use numeral cards or commercially produced cards to encourage children to recognise numerals.

3   Go on a number hunt around the school or classroom.

Plenary

Did the children find any more numbers as they walked around the school? Where did they find them? Where else might they find numbers?

Session 3:

Resources:

Set of large dot cards (for main activity)

Sets of dot cards and numeral cards (for activity 1)

Sets of dot cards (for activity 2)

Cubes (for towers)

Plastic numerals

Objects to bury in the sand

Starter

Play 'Thumbs up'. Make a statement, for example 'Four is smaller than six', 'Eight comes before nine', 'Three is bigger than five', 'Seven comes between five and eight'. If the children agree with the statement, they put their thumbs up, if not they turn their thumbs down.

Main teaching activity

Share the dot cards amongst the children. Draw three squares in a row on the board. Ask: 'Who is holding the card with six dots?' Attach the card to the right-hand square. 'Who has got the card with four dots?' Attach the card to the left-hand square. Write the numbers underneath the squares. Say the numbers together. As you do this, point to the square containing four, move your finger slowly across the empty box, then point to six and say the number six. Who can tell you what number is missing? What number comes between four and six? Repeat using other numbers (for this part of the session, limit the answer to just one possible number).

Group activities

1   Put out a line of dot cards in order. Remove one card. Can they tell you which one is missing? How did they work it out? Repeat several times, removing other numbers. Now replace the dot cards with numeral cards. Repeat the process.

2   Can the children order a set of dot cards when a card has been removed? Make a cube tower of the missing number.

3   Bury numeral cards or plastic numbers in the sand tray. Find the numbers and match objects to that number.

Plenary

Discuss the activities. Put two numbers on the board, for example six and eight, three and five. Say the number names. Can the children tell you what number is missing?

Session 4:

Resources:

Large sheet of paper divided into three vertical columns
Die
Numeral cards, washing line and cubes (for towers)
Set of dot cards

Starter

Play 'Thumbs up' as in session 3.

Main teaching activity

As for session 3 but introduce the possibility of more than one number that comes between, for example select the numbers one and four. What numbers could go in the middle square?

Group activities

1   Divide a large sheet of paper into three vertical columns. Roll a die. Record the score in the central column. Can the children give you a number that is more/greater than the number? Record the answer in the right-hand column. Now can they tell you a number that is less? Repeat, so all children have an opportunity to roll the die.

2   Ask children to order numeral cards in ascending order (they may need a number line to support this). Make towers to correspond to the numerals.

3   Can the children order a set of dot cards when a card has been removed?

Plenary

Attach the number cards to the washing line in the correct order. Miss out two consecutive numbers. Start at the beginning and say the numbers as you point to them. Can the children say which two numbers are missing? Repeat, missing out two different consecutive numbers.

Session 5:

Resources:

Counting Rhymes by John Foster (Oxford University Press)
Set of large numeral cards and washing line
Two sets of dot cards
Paper copies of dot cards, paper and glue
Pots (two per child) and cubes or counting objects
Labels saying 'more' or 'less'
Set of containers

Starter

Read 'One, two, three four' (from *Counting Rhymes*). Play 'Show me'. Say a number and ask children to hold up the corresponding number of fingers. Progress to more complex instructions such as 'Show me one more than four', 'Three and one more'.

Main teaching activity

Use the large numeral cards, shuffle them and identify all the numerals up to ten. Start at zero and count up to ten and back. Put all the cards on the floor, ordered one to ten. Attach the numbers to the washing line as a child answers the appropriate questions, for example 'Which is the smallest number?' One. 'Which is the largest number?' Ten. 'What number is one less than ten?' Nine. 'What number is between six and eight?' and so on.

Group activities

1   Mix two sets of dot cards together and place them face down on the table. Children take two cards. Can they say which is the smallest/largest number? They then take a third card. Now which card shows the largest/smallest number? Can they think of a number that is smaller/greater than their smallest/largest number?

2   Using paper copies of dot cards, give the children three cards for them to order. Can they draw their own dot card that has more dots? Let them stick the cards onto paper in the correct order.

3   Children have two pots. They count out cubes (or other objects) into the pots, and say how many are in each pot. Ask them to put labels on the pots saying 'more' or 'less' or explain their ideas.

Plenary

Discuss activities 2 and 3. Prepare a set of containers: one containing three cubes, another containing six cubes. Put an empty container between the two pots. This will hold any amount of cubes between three and six. Ask how many cubes could be in this pot.

Counting, adding and subtracting

Unit 8

Objectives:

Count reliably up to 15

Recognise numerals one to five

Recognise small numbers without counting

Relate addition to combining two, then three groups

Relate addition to counting on

Vocabulary:

number, zero to 20 and beyond

before, after, next, How many?, missing, start at, count, count on, count up to, count out, and, add, more, makes, equals, altogether, different, total

References:

National Numeracy Strategy pages 2-9, 14-17

Curriculum Guidance for the Foundation Stage pages 68, 69, 74-77

Session 1:

Resources:

Large numeral cards and washing line
Counting Rhymes by John Foster (Oxford University Press)
Large 2 x 3 grid
Five cubes per child
Bingo cards featuring numbers up to five (use numbers up to ten if children need challenging)
Numeral cards (one to five)
Drawing materials

Starter

Place the large numeral cards on the floor in random order. Ask a child to find zero. Peg this onto the washing line. Ask: 'What number comes after zero?' Ask a child to peg the number onto the line. 'What number will come next?' Continue until number five is on the line. (Although this week's objective only states recognising numerals to five it is important to give children the opportunity to go beyond until ten are on the washing line.) Once the numbers are on the number line, ask which number comes before/after/a given number or between two given numbers.

Main teaching activity

Read the poem 'One little kitten' from *Counting Rhymes* by John Foster.

Make a large 2 x 3 grid and write numbers zero to five on it at random. Give children five cubes each. Say a number and get the children to make a corresponding tower of cubes. Ask a child to find the number on their card. Draw a circle around the number. Repeat, using all the numbers.

Group activities

1   Play bingo, using individual cards with numbers up to five (up to ten if children need challenging).

2   Children have a set of numeral cards (one to five) to order and draw corresponding pictures.

3   Make a series of pictures to illustrate the poem for a display. Set out like a staircase (as in the book).

Plenary

Read 'One little kitten'. Count the pictures they have drawn for activity 3.

Ask children to be the teacher - one points to a number, the rest identify it and make a tower of corresponding cubes.

Session 2:

Resources:
Large numeral cards
Tray, cloth and objects to count (on the tray)
Several sets of numeral cards (zero to five) for group activities
A die
Cubes or counting objects, containers and items for sorting
Set of dot cards

Starter

Ask six children to come to the front of the class. Give each child a numeral card. As you give them a card, identify the numeral. Ask: 'Who is holding zero?' Begin a human number line. 'What number will come next?' 'Who is holding that number?'

Main teaching activity

Choose a variety of objects (no more than five). Before the lesson put three on the tray and cover them with a cloth. Tell the children that you are going to let them have a quick look at the things on the tray. Explain that you want them to tell you how many things they can see by holding up that number of fingers. Repeat, changing the number of objects on the tray.

Group activities

1   Give children a set of numeral cards zero to five. Roll the die. Ask the children to look at the die and respond quickly to the question: 'How many spots can you see?' Repeat this several times. Tell them that you are going to play a game. The children take turns at rolling the die, recognising the amount of dots and turning over the corresponding numeral card.

2   Play Pelmanism using numeral cards zero to five.

3   Give children a set of numeral cards (some children may not be ready for numerals up to five, so give up to three if appropriate). Attach numerals to the containers for the children to put in the appropriate number of items.

Plenary

Give each child a numeral card. Hold up a dot card for a few seconds. If they have a corresponding number they hold it in the air. Repeat. At the end of the plenary, hold up a numeral card and the children hold up a matching numeral card and shout 'Snap!'

Session 3:

Resources:
Large numeral cards
Numeral cards (one to five)
Tom Thumb's Musical Maths (A & C Black)
Selection of cubes and a die
Sets of dominoes
Two dice (for plenary)

Starter

Distribute numeral cards one to five amongst the children (one per child). Hold up number one. Any child who has number one holds their card in the air. Repeat up to and including number five, then choose numbers at random, saying 'Stand up if you have got number two'. (They then sit down.) 'Stand up if you have got number five.'

Main teaching activity

Sing 'Hippity Hop' (from *Tom Thumb's Musical Maths*). Ask the children to use fingers to carry out simple addition: 'Hold up one finger on one hand and three fingers on the other hand. How many fingers are you holding up?' Encourage them to touch their nose with each finger as it is counted. Repeat using different amounts.

Group activities

1   Put a selection of cubes in the centre of the group, then roll a die. How many spots can they see? They count out the corresponding amount of cubes. Ask: 'How many cubes have you got?' Roll the die again and get the corresponding number of cubes. How many cubes have they got altogether? Repeat this activity, allowing the children to roll the die and encouraging them to check their counting.

2   Children have two different coloured sets of cubes. They need to make towers of seven using both colours. Can they find different ways?

3   Using sets of dominoes, find the ones with a total of six dots altogether.

Plenary

Show the children two dice. Look at the different ways you can throw a total score of seven. As you do this, refer to activity 2. Have they got any different ways of making seven? Discuss activity 3.

Session 4:

Resources:
Glove puppet and objects to count

Simple outlines of coats with different numbers of buttons (one to five)

Coloured cubes for towers

Objects to bury in the sand tray

Starter

Use the puppet to count objects. As he counts, make sure that he makes mistakes, for example, says two numbers for one object or counts one object twice. Ask children to help him learn. Get them to demonstrate how to move objects and to establish a starting point when counting a group of objects.

Main teaching activity

Show the children a group of items, for example three apples and two plums. Count each group. How many are there altogether? Count all the objects. Repeat this process several times. Model 'Three and two makes five altogether'. Introduce a third group of items, for example two pears. Explain that you want to find out how many pieces of fruit there are altogether. Count the number in each group and record it, for example three add two add two makes seven. Explain that instead of writing words we can use special symbols: $3 + 2 + 2 = 7$

Group activities

1   Use the coat outlines with different numbers of buttons. Children take two coats each. Ask: 'How many buttons altogether?' (You may find it useful with some children to cover each button with counters and then move them so they can be counted more easily.) Progress to asking the children to choose three coats and count how many buttons there are altogether. Use the language of addition, for example 'Two add three add one makes ...', 'Two plus three plus one equals ...'.

2   As for session 3 but use three colours to make towers of eight or nine.

3   Bury items in the sand. Children need to find seven items but only three types of item, in other words two buttons, two cars, three cubes.

Plenary

Discuss all three activities. Emphasise the different ways that the same total can be achieved. Model the number sentence $2 + 3 + 1 = 6$ as you write it on the board. Say what you are writing and ask the children to repeat the modelled sentence as you point to the numbers and symbols.

Session 5:

Resources:
Large numeral cards and washing line

Numbered carpet tiles

Die (labelled 1, 1, 2, 2, 3, 3)

Cubes for towers and box

Board games which involve counting on, for example 'Farm number track' (photocopiable sheet 23)

Objects to bury in the sand tray

Starter

Count up to 40. Emphasise the 21, 22, 31, 32 pattern.

Using large numeral cards, ask children to arrange them in the correct order on the washing line. Ask children to close their eyes. Remove a card. Which number is missing? Repeat. Next, explain that you want them to start at number five and count up to ten. Then start at three and count up to nine.

Main teaching activity

Using the carpet tiles with large numbers on, lay out a number track from one to ten. Ask a child to stand on number three. Roll the die (numbered 1, 1, 2, 2, 3, 3). Ask the child to take that number of steps (squares) forward. What number have they landed on? 'Three and ____ more makes ____.' Ask another child to come and stand on the number five. Repeat the procedure several times.

Group activities

1   Make a tower of four cubes and get two more (leave them as separate units). Say that you want to find out how many cubes are there. 'How many have I got in the tower?' Four. 'Remember this number.' Show the children the two cubes. 'How many cubes are there altogether?' Hold up the tower and say four, then count out 'five, six'. Put three cubes in a box. 'How many cubes are in the box?' Put in three more. 'How many are there altogether? Three, four, five, six.' Repeat using different amounts.

2   Play board games which involve counting on, for example a track game, snakes and ladders.

3   As for session 4.

Plenary

Arrange a set of large numeral cards (numbers two to five) randomly on the carpet, face down. Ask a child to turn over one card and identify the numeral. Everyone keeps that number in their head and counts on two more. Repeat using other cards.

Shape, space and reasoning

Unit 9

Objectives:

Talk about, recognise and recreate simple patterns, including patterns in the environment.

Use everyday words to describe position and direction.

Vocabulary:

number names (zero to 20 and beyond)

pattern, repeat, repeating, continue, different, match, draw

shape, square, circle, triangle, rectangle, star, corner, straight, curved, edges

instruction, position, behind, on top of, in front of, in between, next to, next, top, bottom, middle, above, below

References:

National Numeracy Strategy pages 24-27, 18-19

Curriculum Guidance for the Foundation Stage pages 69, 78-81

Session 1:

Resources:

Tom Thumb's Musical Maths (A & C Black)
Selection of wallpaper/wrapping paper
Selection of coloured 2-d shapes
Fruit or vegetables, paper and paint for printing

Starter

Sing 'Stamp and clap' from *Tom Thumb's Musical Maths*. Clap different patterns. Can the children copy and continue the pattern? Show the children a selection of wrapping paper/wallpaper/material. Can they see the pattern and the way it repeats? Cut a strip off the wrapping paper and cut it into several pieces. Shuffle the pieces. Try and rearrange the pieces to continue the pattern.

Main teaching activity

Using a large set of shapes in different colours, show the children how to make repeating patterns. While you are making the pattern, ask the children to describe it, using colour and shape names. Ask them to predict what will come next.

Group activities

1   Give children one shape in different colours. Ask them to copy and continue the pattern.
2   Give children two different shapes in two or three different colours. Ask them to copy and continue the pattern.
3   Use different fruit/vegetables cut in half to print repeating patterns.

Plenary

Discuss the patterns made in the three activities.

Session 2:

Resources:

Tom Thumb's Musical Maths (A & C Black)

Pictures/objects depicting patterns (chosen to represent different cultures)

2-d shapes in the same colour

Seeds/ dried vegetables

Wallpaper/ wrapping paper

Starter

Sing 'Stamp and clap' from *Tom Thumb's Musical Maths.* Clap different patterns. Can the children copy and continue the pattern?

Main teaching activity

Show the children the pictures of patterns/patterned objects. What shapes can they see? How many colours can they see? Can they guess where they would see these patterns - in a building, on clothing, on carpets, and so on?

Group activities

1   Give children two or three shapes in the same colour. Ask them to copy and continue the pattern.

2   Use a variety of seeds and dried vegetables to make patterns from different cultures, for example Celtic borders, designs for Arabic/oriental rugs.

3   Cut the sheet of wrapping paper/wallpaper into squares (no smaller than 3 x 3 cm). Ask the children to rearrange the squares to match the pattern.

Plenary

Look at the patterns made in all three activities. Have they managed to recreate the wrapping paper? Put two edges of wallpaper together. Does the pattern match? Show the children how you have to adjust the paper so that the pattern continues.

Session 3:

Resources:

Rosie's Walk by Pat Hutchins (Puffin)

A collection of small toys and a box

Three shoe boxes turned on their side and taped together to create a small shelf unit and at least 12 small toys/ objects to fit onto the shelves

3 x 3 grids

Pictures/shapes

Tape recorder or language master (giving simple instructions using positional language)

Shape templates and crayons

Paper and drawing materials

Starter

Read *Rosie's Walk* by Pat Hutchins. Discuss the route around the farm.

Main teaching activity

Use a collection of small toys and a box. Give instructions to the children, for example 'Put two toys *in* the box', 'Put one toy *behind* the box', 'Stand two toys *next to* each other'. Ask a child to place another toy *in between* them. Introduce the box shelves. Ask a child to arrange all 12 toys on the shelves. How many toys are on the top shelf, the bottom shelf and the middle shelf? Explain to the children that you are going to describe the position of a toy and they have to identify which one it is. For example, 'What toy am I thinking of? It is on the top shelf/it is next to/it is in between/it is above ....' . (You don't have to specify what shelf it is on.)

Group activities

1   Using a 3 x 3 grid, children place pictures or shapes in the appropriate position. (You might prefer children to draw in the squares.) For example, 'Put a square in the middle box', 'Put a triangle above the square', 'Put a rectangle next to the triangle'. Discuss how there are two possibilities. Introduce right and left. (Remember, the left hand forms a capital L if they hold it in front of them.) Continue until all of the grid is completed.

2   Children work in pairs, with a tape or language master giving simple instructions: 'Draw around the circle', 'Draw a triangle above the circle', 'Draw a rectangle next to the circle' and so on. Provide simple templates for the children to draw around. Children compare the pictures they have drawn. Are they the same?

3   Children make pictures for display about Rosie's walk.

Plenary

Highlight today's vocabulary. Ask a child to come to the front and follow some simple instructions (you may wish to specify the toy the child chooses): 'Put toy one on the middle shelf'. 'Take toy two and put it above toy one.' 'Toy three - put it next to toy one.' Continue until all the toys are on the shelf.

Session 4:

Resources:
Numeral cards
Paper and pen for main teaching activity
Shoe-box shelves (made for session 3)
Selection of play food
Language master and shape templates (as for session 3)
Paper and drawing materials

Starter

Play 'Show me'. Hold up a numeral card and children hold up the corresponding number of fingers. 'Show me one less than three/one less than six/a number smaller than four' and so on.

Main teaching activity

Tell the story of 'Little Red Riding Hood'. Begin by drawing a house in the top left-hand corner of a sheet of paper. This is Little Red Riding Hood's home. In the bottom right-hand corner draw Grandma's house. Ask the children what things she might see *en route*. She might go through a gate, walk over a bridge, cross a road, go along the path, and so on. Draw the features that the children suggest.

Group activities

1   In Grandma's house is a cupboard. Using the shoe-box shelves, let the children tell you where to put the play food objects in the cupboard. For example, a child chooses an object and says 'Put it on the top shelf', 'Put it next to …'

2   As for session 3.

3   Make a large picture for display of Little Red Riding Hood's route to Grandma's house. Label with key positional words, for example 'through the gate', 'over/across a bridge', 'behind a tree', 'in the house'.

Plenary

Ask the children to retell Little Red Riding Hood's route to Grandma's house.

Session 5:

Resources:
Glove puppet
Large (A3 size) target board, laminated
Numeral cards (one card per child - zero to eight)
Paper copies of numeral cards (zero to eight)
Bean bag
Target board (made from carpet tiles)

Starter

Sing 'Ten green bottles'. Use the puppet to count up to 20 but miss out or mispronounce numbers, for example, say 'fiveteen, sixteen, seventy'. Can the children help him learn the correct number names and order? Count beyond 20. When the puppet gets to 29, the next number he says is 20 10. Can the children correct him?

Main teaching activity

Make a large (A3 size) target board using numerals zero to eight (see diagram) and laminate it. (This resource will be used a lot in the starter sessions during the summer term.)

5	1	8
7	6	2
4	0	3

Identify all the numerals, then ask the children 'Tell me a number next to one/above zero/below six' and so on.

Group activities

1   Give each child a numeral card. Refer to the target board and identify all the numerals. They are not in the correct order as in a number line. Play 'Show me'. Say a number. Children hold up their numeral cards if they match. 'Hold up your card if your number is on the top row.' 'Hold up your card if it is below the number seven.' 'Hold up your card if your number is in the middle square.'

2   Give children paper photocopies of numeral cards. Let them arrange the numerals to make their own target board.

3   You will need a bean bag and a large target board made from carpet tiles. Children, working with an adult, take it in turns to throw the bean bag and identify what number square it lands in. This activity can be extended by the adult recording each child's score, or a child selecting the appropriate numeral card. The first child to collect six different numbers is the winner.

Plenary

Use a target board made by one of the children. Ask a child to identify the number in the middle square. What number is below/above/next to it?

Counting and measures including time

Unit 10

Objectives:

Recite the number names in order, counting on or back from ten or nine

Recognise numerals one to nine

Make direct comparisons of two then three or more lengths or masses

Know the days of the week in order

Vocabulary:

number names (zero to 20), count, count up to, begin counting from, count back from, What number comes next?

order, sort, heavy, heavier, light, lighter, balance, weighs, the same, more than

days of the week, Sunday, Monday, Tuesday, Wednesday, Thursday, Friday, Saturday, today, tomorrow, yesterday, day, week, next

References:

National Numeracy Strategy pages 2-9, 22-23

Curriculum Guidance for the Foundation Stage pages 68-69, 74-75, 80-81

Note: During the next ten sessions it would be useful to set up an area in the classroom as a post office.

Session 1:

Resources:

House outlines (with doors numbered one to ten)

Number line to 20

Numeral cards (for playing pairs)

House outlines with one to ten dots on the roof, door outlines (numbered one to ten)

Boxes for sorting office

Envelopes numbered one to ten (initially)

Starter

Explain that today you are going to count up to ten, but instead of starting at one you are going to begin counting from number three. Say number three, then continue the count, making sure that they stop at ten. Repeat, starting at five and then with four. Count up to ten and stop. What number comes next? Continue the count. Repeat, starting the count at nine.

Main teaching activity

Using simple house outlines, tell the children that you want them to help you make a street. Can they put the houses in the correct order? When number nine is in position, ask 'What number comes next?' (Use a number line to 20 as a point of reference.) Can they find the number ten? What number will come next? Continue up to 15.

Group activities

1 Play Pelmanism (pairs) with numeral cards. Make sure that the children can tell you the number names as they turn over the cards.

2 Using more house outlines but this time put dots onto the roofs with values one to ten. Can children order the house outlines? Can they put the corresponding numbered doors onto the houses?

3 Create a sorting office for the post office. Children can empty post boxes and sort the numbered envelopes according to the house numbers.

Plenary

Have a variety of numbered envelopes and ask the children to identify which house the letters should be delivered to.

Give each child a door outline and ask them to find out their home door number and get an adult to write it for them.

Session 2:

Resources:
Counting Rhymes by John Foster (Oxford University Press)
Large blank number line
Numeral cards zero to ten
Bingo cards (zero to ten)
House outlines and numbered doors
Sorting boxes and envelopes, paper clips

Starter

Children sit in a circle. Read 'Countdown' from *Counting Rhymes* by John Foster.

Count up to 20. Count up to ten. Now start counting back in ones from ten to zero. Start at nine and count back. Start at ten and count back around the circle. Start at nine and count back to zero.

Main teaching activity

Have a large blank number line and attach zero, one, three, four, six, seven, nine and ten. Identify the numbers that are on the number line. Can the children tell you which numbers are missing? How do they know where the number two should go?

Group activities

1 Play bingo. Turn over a pile of numeral cards, one by one, calling out each number. If the children have the number, they cover it with a counter. Turn your card around so the children can see the number. Say, for example, 'This is number three. Cover the number three'. (This gives the children who do not know what the numeral looks like the opportunity to match the numerals.)

2 Give children a row of house outlines. Can they put the numbered doors onto the houses in the correct order?

3 As for session 1.

Plenary

Do activity 2 as a class activity. Take the sorted envelopes and paper clip all the same numbers together. Can the children put the packs of envelopes in the correct order, to make it easy to deliver the letters?

Session 3:

Resources:
Glove puppet
Large numeral cards and washing line
Numeral cards (one for each child)
Selection of heavy and light parcels (make sure that at least one small parcel is heavy and a larger one is light)
Pan balances
Small box as a weight
Cubes, sand or rice for balance weights

Starter

With the help of the puppet, put the large numeral cards onto the washing line in this order: zero, two, one, three, four, six, five, seven, eight, nine. Say the numbers out loud. Is he correct? Ask the children to help him put the numbers in the correct order. Say the numbers as you point to them. Give each child a numeral card. Explain that you are going to say a number. If they have that number on their card, they hold their card in the air. Point to the number on the line. Is it the same?

Main teaching activity

In the post office there are some parcels. Some are heavy and some are light. Let the children hold two parcels, one in each hand. Make sure that one is considerably heavier. Children identify the heavy parcel and the light parcel. Recap on how the scales work. When the pans are level they balance. If it is heavy the pan will go down.

Group activities

1 Use a selection of parcels. Explain that you are going to find out which parcel is the heaviest and which is the lightest. (Make sure that at least one small parcel is heavy and a larger one is light.) Ask a child to pick two parcels. Which is the heaviest? Confirm their decision by using a balance. The next child chooses a parcel. Compare the weight with the heavy parcel. Which is heaviest? Repeat using another parcel. Which is the lightest parcel? 'This parcel is heavier than that one, but it is lighter than this.' Arrange them in a line:

Lightest ⟵－－－－－⟶ Heaviest

2 Give each child a small box that will act as a weight. They put the box into one pan then put cubes, sand or rice into the other pan until they balance.

3 Wrap a variety of parcels in brown paper. Children use balances to find the pairs of parcels that weigh the same (they balance).

Plenary

Discuss today's activities.

Session 4:

Resources:

Counting Rhymes by John Foster (Oxford University Press)

As for session 3 plus numeral cards one to ten (one for each child)

Playdough

Starter

Say the poem 'One little kitten' from *Counting Rhymes*.

Main teaching activity

Give each child a numeral card. Say a number. The children hold up their card. Repeat this several times. Then say 'Show me one more than two', 'Show me one more than four', 'Show me one more than one'. Collect in the cards. Ask ten children to come to the front and give them one numeral card each. Can they put themselves into the correct order?

Group activities

1   As for session 3.
2   As for session 3.
3   As for session 3.

Plenary

Show the children a large piece of playdough. Four children can play with it but, to make it fair, you want all the children to have the same amount. Get children to suggest ways of doing this using a balance.

Session 5:

Resources:

Harlequin (A & C Black)

The Very Hungry Caterpillar by Eric Carle (Puffin)

Days of the week written onto card and laminated

Bingo cards (as for Unit 10, session 2)

Zig-zag books with seven sections

Drawing materials

Starter

Sing 'Each day different' from *Harlequin*.

Main teaching activity

Read *The Very Hungry Caterpillar* by Eric Carle. Say the days of the week, beginning with Sunday. 'What day is it today?' 'What day was it yesterday?' Discuss what the children do on Monday. Show the word Monday. Attach it to the board. 'What do you do on Tuesday?' Show the word and attach it to the board. Continue and arrange the days in a cycle.

Group activities

1   Play bingo (as in Unit 10, session 2).
2   Make a zig-zag book with seven sections. Label each section with a day of the week. Children make their own version of what they could eat during the week.
3   Children draw pictures that show what the hungry caterpillar ate during the week.

Plenary

Discuss activities 2 and 3. Sing 'Each day different'. Look at the cycle of days of the week. 'What day of the week is it today?' Can the children identify the word? 'What day is it going to be tomorrow?' 'What day was it yesterday?'

Counting, adding, subtracting and money

Unit 11

Objectives:

Count reliably up to 20

Recognise numerals zero to nine

Relate addition to counting on

Understand and use the vocabulary related to money

Sort coins: 1p, 2p, 5p, 10p, 20p

Use 1p coins in role play

Sort and match objects, justifying decisions made

Vocabulary:

number, numbers to 20 and beyond, What number ...?, before, after, more, less, order, most, least, continue counting, count on, count out, count back, altogether, add, and, makes, equals, plus, sort, sorting, How many?, How much?

money, coin, penny, pence, worth, price, match, buy, cost, label, amount, sort

References:

National Numeracy Strategy pages 2-9, 14-17, 20-21

Curriculum Guidance for the Foundation Stage pages 63, 64, 74-77

Session 1:

Resources:

Large numeral cards and washing line

Post office resources as for Unit 10, to include envelopes, stationery, pencils and magazines

Set of numeral cards (zero to nine) for each child

Small boxes labelled one to nine and objects for sorting

Starter

Count up to 20 and beyond. Put all the numeral cards in random order. 'What number shall we start with?' Zero. 'What number comes next?' One. 'What is one more than one?' Continue until all the numbers are on the line. Ask the children questions, for example: 'What number comes before/after ....?' 'What number is one more/one less than ....?' Start at nine and count back to zero, pointing to the numbers as they are said.

Main teaching activity

Continue with the theme of the post office. Explain that all the stock needs sorting. Each box of pencils should contain 16 pencils. Give the children a handful of pencils and let the children count them. 'How many are there?' Sixteen. 'How many cards have we got in this box?' Count them out. Seventeen. 'Are there more cards or pencils?' Continue counting out objects. Count out 18 envelopes. Are there more cards or envelopes?

Group activities

1   Give each child a set of numeral cards (zero to nine) and ask them to arrange them in order. Ask them to hold up number one, then replace it. Hold up number two, then replace it. Hold up numbers five, eight, nine and seven.

2   Children do a stock check, counting and checking that there are 16 pencils in each box, 20 envelopes, and so on.

3   Label some small boxes with numbers one to nine. Children count the corresponding number of items into the boxes.

Plenary

Discuss activities 2 and 3. Ask if the correct amount of things were in each box in activity 2 or were there too many or not enough? Ask children to count them out and check.

Session 2:

Resources:

Tom Thumb's Musical Maths (A & C Black)
Laminated target board
Shopping bag or basket and objects for counting
Number line, die and counters
Simple track game (photocopiable sheet 23) and a die
Numbered carpet tiles and die (labelled 1, 1, 2, 2, 3, 3)
Bean bags

Starter

Sing 'Supermarket shop' from *Tom Thumb's Musical Maths*. Count from zero to 20 then extend to 30. Use a target board to identify the starting point. Explain that you are going to say a number and that you want them to continue counting in ones. Demonstrate with, say, five. Ask them to put the number five in their head (encourage them to pat their head and say 'five') then continue counting.

Main teaching activity

Explain that they are getting very good at adding two groups of things by putting all of them together and counting them all. That can take a long time, so now they are going to learn how to add by counting on. Place three objects in your shopping basket and say: 'I have got three things in my basket'. Count the three objects. Tell the children that you are going to get two more. Count out two more items. You now want to find out how many things there are altogether. 'How many things have I got in the basket? Three.' Then count 'four, five', as you point to the other two objects. 'Three and two more makes five altogether, three add two makes five.' Demonstrate how you could record this as 3 + 2 = 5. Repeat using different amounts. It is important that the children see you recording the sum and reading it. Let the children hear you use the words 'and', 'add' and occasionally 'plus'.

Group activities

1   Give each child a number line and one counter. The children take it in turns to roll a die. Put the counter on the appropriate number on the number line. Roll the die again. Starting at the counter, they count on. Ask: 'What number have you got to?' For example, three, count on four. You get to the number seven.

2   Play a simple track/board game.

3   Children create a large number track on the floor using numbered carpet tiles. They take turns to roll a die (labelled 1, 1, 2, 2, 3, 3) and move their bean bag on to the appropriate number tile.

Plenary

Tell the children that you are going to say a number and you want them to count on four more using their fingers. 'Put three in your head (tap your head)' then say four, five, six, seven. 'Put five in your head and count on three.'

Session 3:

Resources:

1p stamps (you can make your own)
Selection of coins to the value of 1p, 2p, 5p, 10p and 20p
2 x 3 grids labelled as shown
Die labelled 1p, 1p, 2p, 2p, 5p and 10p
Small money bags (as used in banks)
Boxes labelled 2p, 5p and 10p
Labels showing 1p, 2p to 10p (draw around the appropriate number of 1p coins on each label)

1p	2p	5p
10p	1p	2p

Starter

Sing 'Five currant buns in the baker's shop'. In the post office you can buy stamps that cost 1 penny each. Show the children three 1p coins. Ask: 'How many stamps can I buy?' Show them six 1p coins. 'How many stamps can I buy?' Show them four stamps. 'How much will four stamps cost?' Ask a child to get the corresponding amount of coins. Show them seven stamps. Count the stamps. 'How much will seven stamps cost?' Ask a child to get the corresponding number of coins. Repeat.

Main teaching activity

Children sit in a circle. Hold up a 1p and 2p coin. Explain: 'These are coins. How much is this coin worth?' One penny. 'How much is this coin worth?' Two pence. 'How much is this silver coin worth?' Five pence. 'Which coin is worth the most?' 'This coin is silver coloured but it's bigger than the 5p. It is worth ten pence.' 'Which coin is worth the most?' Introduce the 20p coin.

Group activities

1   Put a selection of 1p, 2p, 5p and 10p pieces into the centre of the group - enough to cover a 2 x 3 grid for each child. Give each child a grid. They take it in turns rolling the coin die and taking the appropriate coin. The first child to collect all six coins is the winner. Make sure that you question the children about the value of the coins as they select them. For example, 'What coin is it?' 'How much is it worth?'

2   Provide some small money bags. Ask children to count 20 1p pieces into each bag. The other coins can be put into the boxes labelled 2p, 5p and 10p.

3   Children have price labels and match coins to the labels.

Plenary

Discuss activities 2 and 3.

Session 4:

Resources:
Selection of coins (all values)
'Collect 1p' game (photocopiable sheet 26), counters and die
Price labels
Quantity of 1p coins

Starter

Identify a selection of coins and ask the children to order them according to value. (Large laminated coins can be hung on the washing line.) Start with 1p. Ask a child to identify a coin that is worth more than 1p. If a child suggests 5p, ask them to find the 5p coin. Can anyone find a coin that is worth more than 5p? Hold up the 2p. Can they work out where the 2p should go?

Main teaching activity

Put together a price list of five items that can be bought in the role-play shop. Ask a child to choose two items. How much will they cost? How are they going to work this out? Add the two together. (Get the two amounts in coins. Try to work out the total by counting on. Children check the answer by counting all.) Repeat several times with different items.

Group activities

1   Use the 'Collect 1p' game (photocopiable sheet 26). Put a pot of 1ps in the centre of the group. Children take turns to roll the die and move their counter. If they land on a 1p coin, they take a coin from the pot. The first person to collect ten 1p coins wins.

2   Give children some price labels. Ask them to get the appropriate coin or coins and draw around them.

3   Let children play in the post office using up to ten 1p coins.

Plenary

Choose some items from the post office and ask how much they cost. Ask children to come and get the correct amount of money. If it costs 2p, they may choose a 2p coin. Discuss how many coins they will need if they can only use 1p coins.

Session 5:

Resources:
Selection of coins
Bag
Coins (1p, 2p, 5p, 10p and 20p) for each child

Starter

Order coins according to value, starting on the right-hand side. 'Which coin is worth the most?' (20p) 'Which coin is worth the least?' (1p) Put the 1p on the left-hand side and continue adding coins by asking questions, as in session 4.

Main teaching activity

Put a selection of coins in a bag. Children have a 1p, 2p, 5p, 10p and 20p coin. Describe a coin taken from the bag. (Don't let the children see the coin.) Children listen to the description and hold up the corresponding coin, for example 'My coin is silver, it is round and it has a number five on it. What's my coin?'

Group activities

1   Give all the children a selection of coins. Keep a selection yourself. Hold up a 2p coin. Ask the children to find a 2p coin. Ask: 'What number is on the coin?' 'What shape is it?' 'What colour is it?' Repeat with other coins (1p, 5p, 10p and 20p). Give the children an opportunity to sort their coins and then explain the criteria they have used (whether colour, shape or value).

2   Children take a handful of 1p coins, draw around them, then count how many pennies they have.

3   Post office role-play, as in session 4

Plenary

Discuss the reasons children have given for sorting their coins. Give the children a coin each. Ask them to hold up their coin if it is silver coloured, hold up their coin if it is worth 2p, and so on. Discuss activity 2. Ask how many 1p coins they could hold in their hand. Whose hand held the most? How much was their handful worth?

Assess and review

Unit 12

During the spring term, children are beginning to consolidate their understanding and gain in confidence. In this section some of the objectives have been broken down into smaller units. This enables you to decide the next level of experience that the child needs and differentiate activities accordingly.

By the end of Unit 11, most children should be able to:

- Recite number names up to ten/up to 20 and beyond in the correct order
- Count reliably up to and beyond ten objects (It is important to note those children who are unable to count up to ten.)
- Recognise numerals one to five, six to nine or zero to ten
- Say what number comes before, after or lies between given numbers
- Begin to use the vocabulary of addition, for example 'more', 'and', 'add', 'altogether'
- Combine two groups by counting all
- Combine three groups by counting all
- Begin to use the strategy of counting on
- Begin to use the vocabulary of subtraction: 'less', 'left'

- Recognise/sort 1p, 2p, 5p, 10p and 20p coins
- Begin to use 1p coins and get an appropriate amount

- Recite the days of the week in the correct order

- Copy/continue a repeating pattern

- Identify 2-d shapes and use appropriate language to describe them

- Describe two or three parcels using appropriate language (heavy, heavier, light or lighter)

It is important to remember that children may have a passive understanding, but lack confidence to actively use the language required. Therefore opportunities for them to demonstrate their understanding should be included and recorded.

Remember that the information these assessments provide must be used to plan the children's activities at the appropriate level. This may mean revisiting, consolidating or extending the level at which the child is working.

Pages 13 to 15 of *Using Assess and Review Lessons* (DfES 0632/2001) provide examples of questions that can be used to assess a child's understanding against the key objectives.

Note: Children are now entering their final term in the Foundation Stage and need to begin to experience the structure of a dedicated numeracy session with a starter, group activities and a plenary (no more than 45 minutes).

Counting, comparing and ordering numbers

Unit 1

Objectives:

Say and use number names beyond 20 in order in contexts, for example number rhymes, songs, counting games and activities

Use language such as 'more' or 'less', 'greater' or 'smaller' to compare two numbers

Order a given set of selected numbers, for example two, five, eight, one, four

Count reliably to 20 and beyond (objects and other contexts) (continued in Unit 2)

Vocabulary:

number names to 20 and beyond, How many?, more, less, largest, smallest, before, after, order, What comes next/before?

count in ones, count on, count back, order, in between, sort, match

References:

National Numeracy Strategy pages 2-10, 11-13

Curriculum Guidance for the Foundation Stage pages 68, 74, 75

Session 1:

Resources:

Numeral cards (zero to 20) and washing line

Transparent wallets containing small objects for counting

Sticky labels

Four sets of numeral cards (zero to nine)

Selection of large number tiles

Simple board/track games

Starter

Explain that you are going to count in ones up to ten starting from zero. Repeat, counting up to 20. Ask 'What number comes after 20?' Continue the count beyond 30. Distribute numeral cards zero to 20 amongst the children. Using the washing line, attach the numbers to make a number line. Ask questions: 'Who has got zero?' 'Who has got the largest number?' Attach the number ten to the number line. Ask 'What number comes before ten?' and so on.

Main teaching activity

Show children a series of transparent wallets containing small objects. Let the children count the objects. Write the corresponding numbers on labels and stick them to the wallets. Identify the numbers. Explain that you are going to put the wallets in the correct order, starting with the smallest number on the left. 'Which is the biggest/largest number?' Put that wallet on the right. Look at the remaining wallets. 'What number should come next?' 'Have we got that number?' No. Continue questioning until all the wallets have been sequenced.

Group activities

1   Use three sets of numeral cards (zero to nine). Keep each set separate and shuffle them. Put all three piles face down. Children take turns to turn over three cards and put them in order. Extend to using four sets of cards.

2   Put in order a selection of number tiles (smallest first).

3   Give children the opportunity to play simple board/track games.

Plenary

Discuss activity 1, including extension activity and activity 2.

Session 2:

Resources:

Three dice numbered 1 to 6, 7 to 12 and 13 to 18
Four sets of numeral cards (zero to nine)
Selection of number tiles
Simple board/track game
Numeral cards and washing line
Blank cards or paper

Starter

Explain that you are going to count in ones up to ten starting from zero. Repeat, counting up to 20. Now choose someone to say zero, and then count around the circle. Stop the children at regular points, for example when the number five has been said. Ask: 'Who is going to say number eight?' Instead of starting at zero every time, start at ten or 20 and count back around the circle.

Main teaching activity

Use the three numbered dice. Give three children turns at rolling the dice. Record the three numbers scored on three cards. Which is the largest number? Which is the smallest? Explain that you are going to put them in order, starting with the largest number. Repeat using different numbers.

Group activities

1   As for session 1 but using four numbers.
2   Put in order a selection of number tiles (largest first).
3   Play simple board/track games.

Plenary

Choose four different numbers and see if the children can order them, largest first. Choose another four numbers, order them smallest first. Using the washing line, children peg up three numbers between zero and ten in the correct order, starting smallest first. (Leave gaps to allow for other numbers to be added.) Put the remaining cards on the floor. Ask a child to find a number, for example larger than two but smaller than five, and peg it onto the washing line. Find a number smaller than three, and so on. Continue until the line is complete.

Session 3:

Resources:

Set of numeral cards (zero to nine) for each child
Outline of ten houses and doors numbered one to ten
Ten small toys or pictures of animals
Two sets of numeral cards (zero to ten extending to 20)
Strips of numbers written in random order
Paper, scissors and glue
Selection of price labels (for ordering)
Large numeral cards

Starter

Count in ones up to ten, starting from zero. Repeat, counting up to 20. 'What number comes after 20?' Continue the count beyond 30. Give each child a set of numeral cards (zero to nine). (Remind the children that they can look at a number line to help them.) Ask the children to order the cards. Encourage them to set them out as below:

0	1	2	3	4
5	6	7	8	9

This arrangement takes up less space. Some children will need support, by counting and instructing them to find that card. Play 'Show me'. 'Show me number six.' Encourage the children to find the correct card and hold it close to their chest and then upon the command 'Show me!' all the children turn their cards to show you. 'Show me number four!' and so on. Children need to be taught how to replace the cards in their original position.

Main teaching activity

Make a street of ten houses. Put a door numbered five on the fifth house. Use small toys or pictures as inhabitants for each house. Dog lives at number five. His friend, cat, lives at number seven. Ask a child to put number seven door and cat in the appropriate position. Duck lives in between cat and dog. What number house does she live at? Continue until the street is full. 'What number comes before/after five?' 'What number comes before/after seven?'

Group activities

1   Use two sets of numeral cards zero to ten (extend to 20). Spread them face down on the table. Children take turns in turning over two cards. If they are consecutive numbers, the children keep the pair.
2   Give children a strip of numbers in random order. Children cut them into squares and stick them in the correct order onto a strip of paper.
3   Give children price labels to put in the correct order.

Plenary

Put a selection of large numeral cards on the floor for the children to put into the correct order. Discuss where the numbers should go. Can they find any that are consecutive/next door to each other? Find clues that will help them order the numbers.

Session 4:

Resources:
Large number line (photocopiable sheet 7)
Numeral cards (zero to nine) for each child
Eight containers/bags containing eight to 15 cubes or counters
Coloured cubes
Numeral cards or plastic numbers
Selection of dominoes
Large numeral cards (you may want to use a washing line)

Starter

Children sit in a circle. Continue as for session 3 only 'Show me' has the focus of the number before/after. Use the large number line as a point of reference. Give each child a set of numeral cards (zero to nine). Say a number, and ask the children to hold up the number that comes before or after it.

Main teaching activity

Spread numeral cards eight to 15 on the floor. Ask children to help you identify the numbers. Show the children eight different bags/containers which have cubes or counters in them. Explain that you are going to count the objects in each container and match them to the correct numeral card. Give a container to a child and ask them to empty it onto the floor. Encourage the child to move each object as it is counted. Ask another child to find the matching numeral card. Replace the items in the container and attach the numeral. Order the numerals.

Group activities

1   Give children a selection of different cubes. The children count them and sort into groups of matching colours, then match them to numerals (cards or plastic numbers).

2   Give children a selection of dominoes. Count the number of spots and put them in order - smallest first.

3   Give the children large numeral cards (some have been removed). Can they order the numbers (perhaps using the washing line) and find out which cards are missing?

Plenary

Discuss activity 3. What numbers were missing? Check the ordering of the dominoes. Add another domino. Where should this domino go?

Session 5:

Resources:
Numerals cards zero to 20 and washing line
Containers/bags containing eight to 15 cubes or counters
Coloured cubes, numeral cards or plastic numbers
Selection of dominoes
Large numeral cards

Starter

Put all numbers zero to 20 on the washing line. Count and point to the numbers as they are said. Ask the children to close their eyes. Remove numbers four and seven. The children open their eyes. Can they identify which two numbers are missing? Replace the missing numbers. Repeat the process. Then remove three consecutive numbers. Can the children say which numbers are missing?

Main teaching activity

As for session 4 but use only numeral cards 15 to 20 and matching quantities in the containers.

Group activities

1   As for session 4 only progress to put towers and numerals into numerical order.

2   As for session 4 only order starting with the largest number.

3   As for session 4.

Plenary

Display a set of five numbers. 'We are going to put them in order starting with the largest number first. Which is the smallest number?' Can the children work out which numbers are missing?

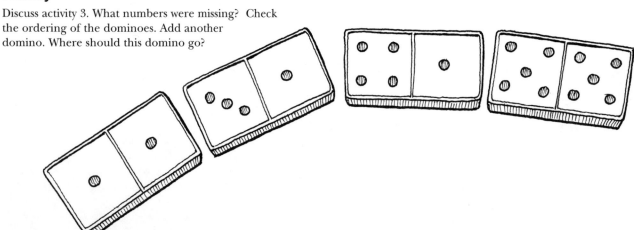

Counting, reading and writing numbers

Unit 2

Objectives:

Count reliably to 20 and beyond (objects and other contexts)

Record numbers by making marks

Begin to relate addition of doubles to counting on

Find a total by counting on when one group is hidden

Vocabulary:

numbers zero to 20 and beyond

count, more than, less than, between, before, after, count on, mark, number sentence, missing, How many?, and, add, equals, altogether, total, double, same as, different

References:

Counting, reading and writing numbers: *National Numeracy Strategy* pages 2-10

Adding and subtracting: *National Numeracy Strategy* pages 14-17

Curriculum Guidance for the Foundation Stage 68, 69, 74-77

Session 1:

Resources:

Large numeral cards zero to 20 and washing line

Pictures/cards or number frieze (commercially produced) showing ten to 20 objects

4 x 5 grid for each child, die and counters (up to 20 per child)

Cubes or counters

Objects to bury in the sand tray

Starter

Tell the children that you want them to count in ones up to ten starting from zero. Repeat, counting up to 20. 'What number comes after 20?' Continue the count beyond 30.

Put the large numeral cards (zero to 20) on the floor in a random arrangement. Children take it in turns to hang numbers on the washing line in the correct order. Ask questions such as 'Tell me a number more than four/a number less than seven/a number more than three but less than six'. You may want to specify one more or one less than a specific number.

Main teaching activity

Show children a series of pictures/cards or a number frieze showing more than ten objects, up to 20. Ask children to count the objects, touching each as it is counted. Use questions to enhance their understanding of value: 'Are there more rabbits than fish?' 'Is 16 more than 12?' 'Does it make any difference where we start counting?'

Group activities

1 Give each child a 4 x 5 grid. Count how many squares there are. Point to each square as it is counted. Children take it in turns to roll a die, get the corresponding amount of counters and cover the squares. Keep asking the children to count how many counters they have. The first child to reach 20 with an exact throw is the winner.

2 Give children a target number and ask them to get the correct amount of cubes or counters.

3 Bury a variety of objects in the sand tray. Children uncover them and record how many they find by making marks.

Plenary

Discuss today's activities. Check some of the results obtained in activities 2 and 3.
Clap or beat a drum. Can the children count how many claps/beats they have heard?

Session 2:

Resources:

Number track (photocopiable sheet 7) or farm number track (photocopiable sheet 23), die and counters

Outline of double-decker bus and passengers (photocopiable sheet 22)

Dice

Copies of bus outlines for the children to draw on

Starter

Give each child a small number track and some counters. Children respond to instructions by covering the answer with a counter: 'Put your counter on number five', 'Put your counter on number eight', 'Put your counter on a number between one and four'. Extend to numbers up to 20.

Main teaching activity

Make a large copy of the double-decker bus and ten passengers. (If you can laminate it, it makes it easier to stick the figures on with Blu-Tack.) Put three people upstairs and two downstairs. 'How many people are on the bus?' Write this as a number sentence $3 + 2 =$ and say three add two makes ..... Demonstrate by putting three in your head and counting on two using fingers. Children can check the total by counting all the people. Repeat the process using two different numbers. Write the number sentence but use words: _____ and _____ more equals ..... Continue using different numbers.

Group activities

1   Using the large outline of the bus, children take turns to roll the die to decide how many people go upstairs. Roll the die again. How many people are downstairs? Record this as a number sentence. Ask children to work out how many people are on the bus altogether. Use counting on and counting all to check the answers.

2   Children roll a die and record the number of spots. Then they roll the die again. Record the number of spots. How many spots are there altogether? (Record by drawing spots.)

3   Give children an outline of the bus. Ask them to draw ten people on the bus, some upstairs and some down. Explain that at the end of the session you will record the pictures as number sentences.

Plenary

Discuss activity 2. Focus on activity 3. Use various pictures and scribe the number sentences to go with the pictures, for example $5 + 5 = 10$. Say 'There are five people upstairs in the bus and five downstairs. How many people are on the bus altogether?' Repeat, asking the children to provide the information for you to act as scribe.

Session 3:

Resources:

Numeral cards (zero to 20) and washing line

Dominoes (all the doubles and dominoes with totals of one, three, five, seven, nine and eleven spots)

Two set circles

Two sets of numeral cards (zero to five) and plastic numbers

Die, different coloured cubes and plastic numbers

Rectangular pieces of paper (to represent dominoes)

Paint (optional)

Starter

Put all numbers zero to 20 on the washing line. Count and point to the numbers as they are said. Ask the children to close their eyes. Remove numbers four and seven. Ask the children to open their eyes. Can they identify which two numbers are missing? Replace the missing numbers. Repeat the process. Then remove three consecutive numbers. Can the children say which numbers are missing?

Main teaching activity

Distribute dominoes amongst the children. Ask the children to hold up their domino if it has a total of four spots. Put it in one set circle. Ask for a total of seven spots – put it into the other set. Repeat until all the dominoes are sorted into the two categories. Can they notice any patterns? Explain that some have the same number of spots on each side. These are called doubles. For double one, children hold up one finger on both hands. Count them, 'One, two'. Say 'Double two' and children hold up two fingers on both hands. Count them, 'Two, three, four' and say 'Double two is four'. For double three, they hold up three fingers on both hands. Count them, 'Three, four, five, six. Double three is six'.

Group activities

1   Using two sets of numeral cards (zero to five), spread them face down on the table. Children take turns to turn over cards. If they are the same, you or the child records them as a simple number sentence, for example $2 + 2$ (using plastic numbers) and the child works out the answer by counting on.

2   Children roll a die and take that amount of cubes. They then get the same amount of cubes in a different colour. How many are there altogether? Use plastic numbers to record the answer.

3   Give children a number (one to five). Divide a rectangular piece of paper into two squares (to represent a domino). Children make their own double domino. (You can use paint and fold to get a double if preferred.)

Plenary

Look at activity 3. Sort the children's dominoes according to totals. How many spots are on one side? How many spots are there altogether? Find the total by counting on.

Discuss activity 2.

Session 4:

Resources:

Set of numeral cards zero to nine (one per child)

Toy dog/puppy and a box

Ten pictures of bones (simple outlines will do)

Box, cubes and a die

Ten farm animals or similar

Two dice for activity 3

Starter

Children have a set of numeral cards zero to nine and order them (as in Unit 1, session 3). Ask children to hold up a number that is more or less than a given number or a number that comes before or after.

Main teaching activity

Tell a story about a puppy that likes eating bones. Sometimes he buries them in the garden. (Use a box to represent the garden.) Put two bones into the box. Tell the children that Puppy has buried two bones. 'How many bones has he buried?' Two. 'Remember that number. Puppy has got one more bone. He buries that bone as well. How many bones are in the garden altogether?' Ask the children to close their eyes and try to imagine the bones. Check by emptying the box and counting them all. Continue, adding one, two or three bones until ten bones are buried.

Group activities

1   Count four cubes into a box. Children roll a die and take the corresponding number of cubes. How many cubes altogether? Say 'four' and count on. Vary the number of cubes in the box.

2   Give children a set of items, for example ten farm animals. Find different ways of putting them into two fields.

3   Children use two dice and find different ways of making seven.

Plenary

Discuss the various ways of making ten. Record them as number sentences. Children use their fingers to represent the sentences. Hold four fingers up. How many are folded down? Six. Four add six makes ten.

Session 5:

Resources:

Blank number lines

Numeral cards and Blu-Tack

Cardboard box decorated as a hutch

Rabbit cards and numeral cards

Two sets of numeral cards (zero to five) and cubes (activity 1)

Containers and buttons

Dice

Starter

Using an empty number line, write the numbers one and

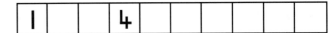

four in the appropriate segments (see diagram). Ask where number three should go. Invite the children to find the number three numeral card and stick it (with Blu-Tack) to the blank line. 'Where will the number six go?' Another child finds the appropriate numeral card and sticks it on. Take a new blank number line and write five and eight in the appropriate positions. 'Where will the number seven go?' 'Where will number four go?' Repeat choosing two different numbers. You may wish to write number seven in the second box and number ten in the fifth box as a challenge. 'Where will numbers six, nine and eleven go?'

Main teaching activity

You will need a box decorated as a hutch. Count three rabbit cards into the box. Ask a child to find the number three and attach it to the box. How many rabbits are in the box? Another two rabbits want to go into the hutch. Count them in. How many rabbits are in there now? Say 'three' and count on two - 'four, five. There are five altogether.' Repeat the activity using different numbers of rabbits.

Group activities

1   Use two sets of numeral cards (zero to five). You keep one set and the children have the other set spread out on the table face down. Pick a card and count out that amount of cubes but hide them, just leaving the card visible. One child turns over a card and gets the corresponding number of cubes. How many cubes are there altogether? Point to your card and begin counting on from that point, touching all visible cubes. Check the answer by counting all the cubes. Record as a number sentence: ___+____=____

2   Give the children two containers. How many different ways can they find of putting seven buttons into the two containers? They can record their answers by drawing.

3   Children use two dice and find different ways of making nine.

Plenary

Discuss activities 2 and 3.

Shape, space and reasoning

Unit 3

Objectives:

Talk about and recreate simple repeating patterns found in the environment and different cultures

Make simple estimates and predictions

Vocabulary:

number, numbers up to 30 and beyond, count, count in ones, count up to, starting from, after, before, How many?, altogether, and, more, less, order, bigger/smaller

pattern, symmetry, symmetrical, same, both, design, repeating patterns, copy, different,

estimate, estimating, guess, enough, not enough, accurate, nearly, almost, check, just over/just under

References:

National Numeracy Strategy pages 18-19, 24-27

Curriculum Guidance for the Foundation Stage pages 74, 75, 78-81

Session 1:

Resources:

Pictures of butterflies, rugs and carpets, kaleidoscopes, mirrors

Strips of squared paper, coloured crayons or felt pens

Pegs and boards for pattern making, pattern cards to copy

Shapes to sequence

Starter

Children use their fingers to count up to ten. Then ask them to hold up three fingers on one hand and two fingers on the other hand. Ask: 'How many fingers altogether?' Encourage the children to touch either their nose or chin with their finger as it is counted. Repeat using differing amounts.

Main teaching activity

Remind the children about previous work that they have done on pattern and symmetry. What was special about a butterfly? The pattern was the same on both sides. Discuss symmetrical patterns found on pottery, rugs, in kaleidoscopes or mirrors. Can they describe the pattern?

Group activities

1   Give the children strips of squared paper and tell them that you want them to have a go at designing scarves. They can only use two colours to make the repeating pattern. Invite some children to make a pattern using three colours.

2   Give children pegs in three colours. Ask them to make repeating patterns. Encourage a 2, 2, 2 or 1, 2, 1 repeat not just simple 1, 1, 1. You may want to give them pattern cards to copy initially as a starting point.

3   Children make simple repeating patterns using two or three shapes.

Plenary

Discuss today's activities. Start a repeating pattern using different sized shapes. Can the children continue the pattern?

Session 2:

Resources:

Patterned material, wallpaper or wrapping paper

Scissors

Different coloured cubes

Pegs and boards for pattern making, pattern cards to copy

Beads and string for necklaces

Starter

Explain that you are going to count in ones up to ten starting from zero. Repeat counting up to 20. What number comes after 20? Continue the count beyond 30.

Clap a pattern. Children repeat. Then demonstrate a pattern using hand/arm actions and the children copy.

Main teaching activity

Choose several pieces of patterned material, wallpaper or wrapping paper. Talk about the pattern. Cut the paper/material in half. Show how the pattern can be broken by not matching the pieces together properly.

Group activities

1   Ask a child to choose three different coloured cubes. Begin a repeating pattern. Can the child continue it? The child then chooses three colours themselves and makes their own repeating pattern.

2   As for session 1.

3   Children thread beads onto a string to create a necklace using a repeating pattern.

Plenary

Discuss today's activities.

Session 3:

Resources:

Numeral cards zero to nine (one set per child)

Large dot cards

Clear container and small objects to put in it

Cards with 'more than ten' written on them (for activity 1)

Small containers and cubes (activity 2)

Sand/water tray, cups, spoons, containers to fill

Starter

Children have a set of numeral cards (zero to nine) to order (as in Summer Unit 1, session 3). Ask children to hold up a number that is more or less than a given number or a number that comes before or after.

Main teaching activity

Tell the children that they are going to learn how to estimate. Explain that sometimes we don't have time to count everything, we have to make a sensible guess. Estimating means making a sensible guess. Tell the children that you are going to show them a large dot card just for a few seconds and they are going to estimate how many dots there are. Show a card with only two dots. 'How many dots did you see?' 'Are you sure there were just two?' Repeat using four dots, then use a larger number. 'Was it as easy to guess the larger number?' 'Was it an accurate/close estimate?'

Group activities

1   Put some objects into a clear container. The children look at the container for a few seconds and then hold up the appropriate numeral card to register their estimate. Give the children an additional card labelled 'more than ten' which they should hold up if they think there are ten or more. Check by counting the objects.

2   Give pairs of children a small container and some cubes. They have to guess how many cubes will fit into the container and tell their partner. Their partner checks the accuracy by counting.

3   Using the sand or water tray, children estimate how many cups, spoonfuls of water/sand it will take to fill a container.

Plenary

Discuss today's activities. How accurate were their estimates?

Session 4:

Small number tracks, such as photocopiable sheet 7 (one per child) and counters
Selection of classroom objects (for estimating quantity)
Tin, with small objects to fit
Containers and cubes (as for session 3)
Sand/water tray, spoons, cups, containers

Starter

Give each child a small number track and some counters. Children respond to questions by covering the answer with a counter. For example: 'Put your counter on a number that is bigger/smaller than four/ten/15/a number that comes before /after three/eight/14'. Extend questions to numbers up to 20.

Main teaching activity

Explain that you are going to find out how useful estimating can be. Tell the children that you need some help getting things ready to use today in the classroom. Five children are going to work on a particular table. They will all need pencils. Have you got enough? Show the children a handful of pencils. Ask for estimates of how many pencils there are. Count them. Who had the most accurate estimate? Repeat using pieces of paper, pairs of scissors, and so on. Ask children to take approximately five counters/pencils, ten crayons, two rubbers, and so on. Is it easier to get a larger number without counting?

Group activities

1   Put a small amount of objects into a tin. Shake the tin. How many objects do they think are in the tin? Record the children's estimates. Empty the tin and count the objects. Who had the most accurate estimate? Repeat using different objects.

2   As for session 3 but change the size of containers.

3   As for session 3 but change the size of containers.

Plenary

As for session 3.

Session 5:

Resources:
Numeral cards (zero to nine)
Whiteboards for each child
Set of dominoes
Containers with objects

Starter

Play 'Show me'. Say a number and the children show the appropriate numeral card. Extend the questions, for example 'Show me one more than seven', 'Show me one less than four'. By now the children should be able to answer simple addition - one add two, two add one, and so on.

Main teaching activity

Estimate the number of children who have school dinners in the class. The children write down their estimate on a whiteboard. Check their answers by counting. Estimate the number of children who have packed lunches and then check. 'How many girls have got short hair?' 'How many boys stay at school for dinner?', and so on. 'Are there more than five/less than five?' 'Who was nearly right with their guess?'

Group activities

1   Place a set of dominoes face down. Turn over a domino for a few seconds. The children write down their estimate of how many spots they saw. Give the domino to a child and ask them to count how many spots there are to check for accuracy. Repeat several times. Children can take the role of the teacher/adult.

2   Put out several containers with objects in. Children guess the amount of objects in the containers, write their estimates, then check by counting.

3   Children work in pairs. One child puts a set of objects into a container and their partner guesses how many. They empty the container and count the objects. The children change roles.

Plenary

Discuss activity 2.

Writing numbers, and measures

Unit 4

Objectives:

Write numerals to five

Count and record larger numbers by tallying

Recognise numerals beyond ten

Compare lengths, masses and capacities by direct comparison

Vocabulary:

numbers zero to 20 and beyond

count, count up, count on, count back, starting at, take away

write, top, trace, before, after, between, bigger, larger, smaller, different, tally, label, which, compare, guess, container, same, shape, size, holds more/most/least, fill, full, empty, emptied, record

References:

Counting, reading and writing numbers: *National Numeracy Strategy* pages 2-10

Measures: *National Numeracy Strategy* pages 22-23

Curriculum Guidance for the Foundation Stage pages 68, 69, 80, 81

Session 1:

Resources:

Numeral cards (zero to ten)
Bingo cards showing numbers up to 20
Objects for counting
Number outlines and tracing paper

Starter

Children use their fingers to count up to ten and back, folding a finger down as each number is said. Children shake their fingers, hide them and respond to 'Show me five fingers!' They shake their fingers and hide them. Say: 'Show me seven fingers!' Repeat for ten fingers. Say that now you are going to take three away: 'Fold down three fingers. How many fingers are still up?' Count them, the children touching their chin/nose as the finger is counted. Reinforce this by saying 'Ten take away three is seven'. Repeat using different amounts.

Main teaching activity

Explain that they are going to learn how to write the numbers one to five this week. Show the children numeral card one. Start at the top and trace over the number. The children then use their 'magic finger' and trace the number in the air. Repeat for numbers two and three.

Group activities

1   Play bingo (using numbers up to 20).
2   Children count objects and write number labels.
3   Children trace over number outlines and practise number formation.

Plenary

Give each child a numeral card up to 20. Call out different numbers and the child with that number stands up. Write in the air numbers one, two and three.

Session 2:

Resources:
Set of numeral cards zero to nine (one per child)
Bingo cards (numbers up to 20)
Objects for counting (as for session 1)
Number outlines and tracing paper (as for session 1)
White boards

Starter
Count in ones up to ten starting from zero. Repeat, counting up to 20. Ask: 'What number comes after 20?' Continue the count beyond 30. The children have a set of numeral cards (zero to nine) and order them (as in Summer Unit 1, session 3). Ask children to hold up a number that comes before/after or in between.

Main teaching activity
Remind the children that yesterday they learned how to write the numbers one, two and three. Briefly recap on the formations covered. Introduce the formation of numbers four and five.

Group activities
1 As for session 1.
2 As for session 1.
3 As for session 1.

Plenary
Say a number up to five, show the numeral card then the children write it (using white boards).

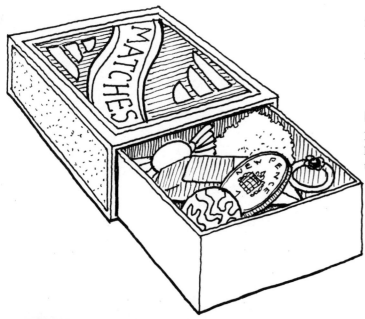

Session 3:

Resources:
Large numeral cards (zero to ten)
Variety of boxes, different sized objects and a small crate
Bean bags (about 13)
Cubes and labels
Matchbox (and items to fit in a matchbox)
Numeral cards (one to 20)

Starter
Using large numeral cards (zero to ten), give a card showing number four to any child and ask them to stand at the front of the class. Ask another child to pick a numeral card. Ask them questions about it: 'Is this number bigger or smaller than number four?' 'Will it come before or after number four on a number line?' Continue inviting children to take cards and position themselves in a human number line, according to their responses.

Main teaching activity
Have a variety of boxes and different sized objects to go into these boxes. Make sure that one box contains three items, another box contains five items, and that there is a small crate containing bean bags (approximately 13). Take things out of the boxes, count and label with the numerals three and five. When emptying the crate, make a tally.

Group activities
1 Let the children pick a box and fill it with non-standard units, such as cubes. 'Which box will hold the most?' The children count the cubes. Scribe for them the numbers for the labels. Can the children order the boxes?
2 How many things can they fit into a matchbox? Count and tally.
3 Give children a numeral card up to 20. Children count out the correct number of items and put them into a box.

Plenary
Discuss all the activities. Who managed to get the largest number of objects into the matchbox? Compare the tally marks.

Session 4:

Resources:
Large empty number line (or draw one on the board)

Collection of containers of different shapes and sand, rice or water to fill

Small cup and a bucket

Sand or rice

Starter

Place a large empty number line on the board (or draw one). Ask a child to point to where zero should go. Ask another child to write zero on the number line. Write the number ten at the opposite end of the line. 'Where should number one go?' Ask a child to write one in the correct place. Continue until all the numbers have been added. You can model the correct way to write numerals beyond five (or this can be an extension activity for specific children). Repeat this activity only begin the line with number ten.

Main teaching activity

Use a collection of containers. Identify the containers and discuss their shapes. Can the children guess which will hold the most? Which will hold the least? How can they find out? Fill one container and empty the contents into another. (Make sure that one container is empty and the other is not full.) Can the children work out which container holds the most?

Group activities

1   Using containers that hold similar amounts but that vary considerably in shape, discuss with the children which they think will hold the most. Why do they think that? How can they find out if one holds more? Fill one container and empty the contents into other containers.

2   Give children a variety of containers. Can they find out which two containers hold the same amount/holds the most?

3   Use a small cup and ask children to count/record by tallying how many cups are needed to fill a small bucket with sand or rice.

Plenary

Discuss the activities. Were the number of cups used in activity 3 to fill the buckets the same? If not, why not? For example, each cup was not full when it was emptied into the bucket.

Session 5:

Resources:
Whiteboards (one per child) and markers

Transparent beakers of the same size, water

Collection of containers

Small cup and a bucket

Sand or rice

Starter

All children have a whiteboard. Demonstrate by drawing a number line on the board. Put zero at the beginning of the line and five at the end. Children draw their own line on their whiteboards and label zero and five. Children mark on the line where number one should go. Remind the children about the formation of the number. Continue until the number line is complete. Children erase the completed line and draw another blank line. They mark on zero and five. Ask them to mark and write where number two goes, show you, then erase the number. Can they mark and write where number four goes? Repeat.

Main teaching activity

Use a set of transparent beakers all the same size. Explain that today, everyone is going to have a drink. Put two different amounts of water into the beakers. Is that fair? No, everyone should have the same. Can they think of any ways of making sure that everyone has the same? Pour one amount into the beaker. Now what do we do? Pour some into another beaker, getting the children to tell you when to stop pouring.

Group activities

1   Using beakers that are the same size, let the children try to pour out equal amounts. You pour the first drink and the children try to put equivalent amounts in the remaining beakers.

2   As for session 4.

3   As for session 4.

Plenary

Discuss today's activities. Did they find it easy to put the same amount of liquid into each beaker? Was it easier to see if there was the same amount standing close to or far away from the beakers? Can the children suggest a way that would make it easier, for example use a small cup and fill it, then empty it into one beaker, refill the cup and empty it into the next beaker, and so on.

Counting, subtracting and money

Unit 5

Objectives:

Count in tens

Recognise numerals beyond ten

Remove a smaller number from a larger and find how many are left by counting back from the larger number

Sort all coins, including £1 and £2, and use in role play

Solve practical problems

Vocabulary:

number, zero to 100

and, add, take away, left, altogether, count on, count back, count up to

more, less, most, least, next

money, coin, penny, pence, worth, price, match, buy, cost, label, amount, value, items, receipt, How many?, How much?

References:

National Numeracy Strategy pages 2-10, 14-17, 20-21

Curriculum Guidance for the Foundation Stage pages 68, 74-77

Session 1:

Resources:

Tom Thumb's Musical Maths (A & C Black)

Cubes for towers

Number tracks (to ten) and ten counters per child (for activity 1)

Die (labelled 1, 1, 2, 2, 3, 3)

Two sets of numeral cards (for Pelmanism)

Set of large numeral cards and washing line

Starter

Count in ones around a circle up to 20. Count in ones back from 20 around the circle. Count in ones all together up to 100. Comment on how long it took to count up to 100. Explain that they are going to learn how to count up to 100 in tens. Ask everybody to show you ten fingers, holding them up in front of them, and say 'ten'. Show them how to fold all their fingers down simultaneously and then stand them up at the same time, this time saying 'twenty' (this is referred to as finger flashing). Repeat until 100 is reached. Repeat, counting up to 100 in tens. Sing the 'Chorus of the centipede' from *Tom Thumb's Musical Maths*.

Main teaching activity

Make a tower of eight cubes. Break off three cubes. Ask how many cubes are in the tower now. Explain that they are going to work out the answer by counting back. 'There were eight. Put the number eight in your head'. Get children to tap their head as they say 'eight'. Show them how to use their fingers to count back, holding up one finger as number seven is said and repeating until three fingers are held up as they say the answer: 'five'. Repeat using a different amount of cubes or objects. Each time reinforce the counting back when objects are removed.

Group activities

1   Each child has a number track (one to ten) and ten counters. Put each counter on a number. Children take turns in rolling a die (labelled 1, 1, 2, 2, 3, 3) and removing the corresponding number of counters.

2   Play Pelmanism using two sets of numeral cards.

3   Children attach large numeral cards to washing line in the correct order.

Plenary

Discuss activity 3. Count back from 20. Starting at seven, count back three using fingers. Point to the numbers on the washing line as you count back. Repeat using different starting points and counting back no more than five. End by singing the 'Chorus of the centipede'.

Session 2:

Resources:

As for session 1 plus large numeral cards (zero to 20), washing line, large number line or track and squares of card/paper, pasta shapes, straws

Starter

Use large numeral cards (zero to 20) and a washing line. Distribute the numeral cards amongst the children. Ask 'Who has got zero?' Peg the card on the left side of the washing line. 'What number comes next?' One. 'Who has got number one?' 'Who has got number 20?' 'Where on the washing line shall we put 20?' Complete the number line by asking questions, such as 'Who has got one more/one less than …?'

Count back from 20, pointing to the numerals as each number is said.

Main teaching activity

Use a large number line or track. Explain that you can use a number line to help you solve 'take away' problems. Remind the children of how they put a number in their head and counted back. Then present them with a situation: 'I have got seven pencils and my friend takes two away. Let's work out how many pencils I have got left. I have got seven (use a label to mark the number seven) and my friend takes two.' Point to the number seven and jump back two. 'What number have I landed on?' Five. (Make sure that the children understand the need to move so as not to count the number seven in the count back.) Repeat the process using different numbers. (This will be revisited in the second half of the term.)

Group activities

1   As for session 1.
2   As for session 1.
3   Children stick ten pieces of pasta onto squares of card or count straws into bundles of ten.

Plenary

Count up to 100 in ones. Then count up to 100 in tens (flash fingers as you count).

Explain that if you had to count 100 pieces of pasta it would take you a long time. Count the pasta on the squares of card. How much is on each card? Ten pieces. If you count in tens it won't take so long. Repeat using straws. Conclude by singing the centipede verse and chorus from *Tom Thumb's Musical Maths.*

Session 3:

Resources:

100 square
Tom Thumb's Musical Maths (A & C Black)
Ten 10p coins
Carpet tiles (zero to ten) and bean bag
Number track for each child (activity 1)
Rabbit counters (reduce rabbit cards - photocopiable sheet 13)
Rabbit cards and die (0, 1, 1, 2, 2, 3)
Card and drawing materials
Large number track

Starter

Count in ones up to 100, using a 100 square as a point of reference. Count in tens up to 100, flashing fingers. Sing the centipede song from *Tom Thumb's Musical Maths.* Show children a pile of ten 10p coins. Ask: 'How much is this coin worth?' Ten pence. Count the coins in tens.

Main teaching activity

Make a large number track with carpet tiles (zero to ten). Ask a child to stand on number five. Mark the square with a bean bag. 'Take two steps back along the line. What number are you on now?' Three. Reinforce the idea that the number five square was not counted in the two steps. Record as 5 - 2 = 3. Repeat using different starting points.

Group activities

1   Each child in the group has a number track. Give each child a rabbit counter (small rabbit card). Explain that he is going to jump back along the numbers. 'Rabbit lives at space number four.' Children draw a circle around the number. 'Put the rabbit on the square. He makes two jumps back. What number is rabbit on now?' 4 - 2 = 2

2   Give each child ten rabbit cards. The children put all ten cards face up, roll the die and turn over that number of cards. The first child to have all their cards face down is the winner.

3   Children write or trace over numerals one to ten on pieces of card. They then work in pairs to play snap or Pelmanism (pairs).

Plenary

Write a number sentence on the board, for example 5 - 3 =

Use the large number track (from the main teaching activity). Ask if anyone can demonstrate what number we need to stand on and how many jumps to go back?

Session 4:

Resources:

Selection of coins (about three per child), to include 50p, £1 and £2

Objects with price labels (1p to 5p)

Coin track game (photocopiable sheet 27)

Ten 1p coins per child (for activity 1)

Coins for sorting

Containers labelled with coin values

Small pieces of paper for receipts

Large receipt (you will need to make this) showing three items

Starter

Children sit in a horse-shoe shape. Give them a selection of three coins each. Hold up a 1p coin. Say: 'This is worth 1 pence. If you have a 1 pence coin, hold it in the air.' Hold up a 2p coin. 'How much is this coin worth? If you have got a 2 pence coin, hold it up.' Repeat the process up to and including 20p. Introduce the 50p, £1 and £2 coins. Ask the children if they have a £1 coin to hold it up.

Main teaching activity

Show children the shop and price labels. Ask a child to pick two items. Ask how much it will cost altogether if you buy both items, for example an apple that costs 3p and a pear that costs 2p. 'What do we do next, to find out how much altogether? That's right, we have to add both amounts together.' Emphasise the numbers three add two more. Can they work it out? Encourage them to use various strategies, counting on or using fingers to represent amounts. Repeat using different items.

Group activities

1   Play the coin track game. Each child starts with ten 1p coins. If you land on a coin you put it in the centre of the table. The first child to put all ten in the centre is the winner.

2   Put a selection of coins into containers. Children sort them according to value.

3   Let children play shops. Price items up to 5p. Children can choose two items. How much will the two items cost? Children make a receipt for the two items and record the total by drawing around coins.

Plenary

Choose a receipt made by one of the children. Look at the prices of the two items. Can the children recognise which two items were bought? Check the total. Repeat using other receipts. Show the children a receipt with three items on. How can you work out how much all three items will cost? Ask for the containers used in activity 2. Hold up a coin from each pot. Children identify its value then empty the contents of one container. Can children spot whether any coins have been put into the wrong container?

Session 5:

Resources:

Assortment of coins (all denominations)

Assortment of coins for the children (two x 1p, two x 2p, two x 5p and one 10p per child)

You (the teacher) need coins to include at least ten 1p coins, 2p and 5p

Coin track game (photocopiable sheet 27) You may want to make tokens/pictures of the objects bought.

Shopping lists with two items on each

Role-play shop

Starter

Children arrange coins in order of value. (You can stick them on the board with Blu-Tack.) Which coin is worth the most: a coin worth more than 10p, a coin worth less than 50p, a coin worth more than 50p?

Main teaching activity

Give each child two 1p, 2p and 5p coins and one 10p coin. Show the children a 1p coin. Can they hold up 1p? Show the children two 1p coins. 'How much are they worth?' Two pence. Can they hold up a coin with that value? Repeat using five 1p coins and ten 1p coins. Hold up a 2p coin. 'What is 1p more than 2p?' Repeat using 5p.

Group activities

1   Play the coin track game (photocopiable sheet 27). Give each child ten pence in 1p coins. Children buy items as they land on the appropriate square.
     When they land on an item, ask the children the following questions: 'How much money have you got?' 'How much does____ cost?' 'How much money have you got left?'

     (You may want to make tokens/pictures of the objects being bought.) The winner is the first person to spend their 10p.

2   Give children shopping lists with two or three items and prices on them. Children get the correct amount of coins and put them into a container with the list.

3   Play shops, as in session 3.

Plenary

Discuss activity 2. Ask a child to count out ten 1p coins. Draw a large purse on the board. Stick the coins to the board. Explain that you are going to find out what you can buy in the shop for 10p. Ask a child to choose an item and remove the appropriate amount of 1p coins. Work out how much is left by counting back. Another child chooses another item. 'Now how much money have we got?' 'How much does it cost?' Remove the 1p coins. 'How much is left?' Encourage children to think about which item or items they could buy and which ones they couldn't afford.

Assess and review

Unit 6

After these sessions, you will be aware of those children who have met or partially met the objective. You may decide to focus on this objective in some oral/mental starters for a few weeks.

By the end of Unit 5, most children should be able to:
■ Say and use number names beyond 20 in order in context, for example number rhymes
■ Count reliably to 20 and beyond
■ Count in tens up to 100 and back

■ Recognise numerals beyond ten
■ Record number by making marks
■ Write numerals to five
■ Count and record larger numbers by tallying

■ Use language - more/less, greater/smaller - to compare two numbers
■ Order a given set of selected numbers, for example two, five, eight, one, four

■ Begin to relate addition of doubles to counting on
■ Find a total by counting on, when one group is hidden
■ Remove a smaller number from a larger number and find how many are left by counting back
■ Make simple estimates and check by counting

■ Talk about and recreate simple repeating patterns

■ Recognise/sort all coins including £1 and £2 coins

■ Recognise which container holds the most/least

Pages 13 to 15 of *Using Assess and Review Lessons* (DfES 0632/2001) provide examples of questions that can be used to assess a child's understanding against the key objectives.

Remember that the information these assessments provide must be used to plan the children's activities at the appropriate level. This may mean revisiting, consolidating or extending the level at which the child is working.

Counting, comparing and ordering numbers

Unit 7

Objectives:

Estimate a number up to ten and check by counting

Write numerals to ten

Begin to understand and use ordinal numbers in different contexts

Vocabulary:

number, write, zero, one, two, three ... to 20 and beyond

guess, estimate, check, How many ... can you see? too many

order, first, second, third, fourth ... tenth, last, next, before, after, between

References:

Counting, reading and writing numbers *National Numeracy Strategy* pages 2-10

Comparing and ordering numbers *National Numeracy Strategy* pages 11-13

Curriculum Guidance for the Foundation Stage pages 68, 74-77

Session 1:

Resources:

Large numeral cards (zero to 20) and washing line

Pencils and other objects for estimating

Cubes and container

Numeral cards (zero to nine) for each child (activity 1)

Sorting trays with different amounts of objects

Small squares of paper for labels

Sand tray

Glue sticks and sand

Dot cards (zero to seven)

Individual whiteboards or laminated card

Starter

Count in ones up to 50 and beyond. Distribute the large numeral cards amongst the children. Start at zero and sequence them up to 20 on the washing line. Now ask the children to close their eyes while you remove a number. Can the children tell you which number is missing? Replace the number. Children close their eyes while you remove another number. Repeat the process. Extend the activity by removing two numbers.

Main teaching activity

Show the children a handful of pencils. Explain that sometimes we have to make a sensible guess, an estimate, rather than count the objects. Can anyone estimate how many pencils you have? (Use questions to help them make their estimates, for example 'Are there more than two?' 'Do you think there are enough for all the children in green group?) Take different ideas, and record the amounts suggested on the board. Count the pencils. Who had the closest estimate? Repeat using other objects.

Group activities

1   Tell the children that you are going to show them some cubes and you want them to estimate how many there are. Show the children a container with four cubes in. First, ask them to choose their answer from one of their numeral cards. Next time, they are going to have a go at writing their answer. Model writing the numbers six and seven. Children write the numbers in the air. Show them another group of cubes. Ask them to write down their estimate. Observe the way in which the children form their numerals.

2   Count the number of items in each component of the sorting tray. Write number labels for each component.

3   Children trace number outlines in the sand with their fingers (zero to five, or up to seven). Use a glue stick to write a number on a piece of paper. Sprinkle sand over it to make a tactile number.

Plenary

Show the children dot cards (up to the value of seven). The children count the number of dots and write the number on their whiteboards.

Session 2:

Resources:
Numeral cards (zero to nine) – one set per child
Large dot cards
Large numeral cards
Whiteboards or paper
Cubes
Dot cards

Starter

Give each child a set of numeral cards (zero to nine) to put in the correct order. Ask them to show you different numbers, for example: 'Show me number six!' Encourage children to replace the card in the correct position. Continue by saying: 'I am going to say a number. I want you to hold up the number that is one more'.

Next, ask children to show you the number eight. Model writing the number. The children use their fingers to trace over the number on their numeral card. Do this several times. Children then draw the number in the air. Continue by saying: 'Show me the number that is one more than eight'. Model how to write the number and the children trace it with their finger, as with the number eight.

Main teaching activity

Using large dot cards, briefly show the children a card and ask them to write down on their whiteboards their guess/estimate of how many dots there are. Is it easier to guess the amount if there are only a few dots?

Group activities

1   Take a set of large numeral cards and shuffle them. Turn over a card and ask the children to write that number on a whiteboard or paper.

2   Children work with a partner. One child makes a tower and their partner has to estimate how many cubes are in the tower. They write their estimate, then count the cubes to check. Then it's their turn to make the tower while the other child estimates.

3   Give children a selection of dot cards. Children write the numbers to go with them.

Plenary

Discuss activities 2 and 3.

Session 3:

Resources:
Numeral cards (zero to ten)
Selection of toy vehicles for ordering
Beads made into a necklace
Blank grids (3 x 3)
Dot cards
Two dice with dots (one labelled one to six, the other die the same but cover the five and six and mark zero)

Starter

Sing 'Ten in the bed'. Emphasise the word 'ten' and explain that they are going to learn how to write the number ten. Practise the formation of the number. Stress the importance of the zero. Count back from ten to zero. Count back again but this time ask the children to hold up ten fingers, say 'ten', then fold one finger down saying, 'One less is nine', fold another finger down – 'One less is eight' – and continue until they reach zero. Take a set of numeral cards and ask children to put them in the correct order. Continue by explaining that you are going to say a number and you want them to show you a number that is one less.

Main teaching activity

Create a traffic jam with toy vehicles. Mark a white line at the beginning of the traffic queue. Move each vehicle across the white line, stating its position - first, second, and so on. Ask which vehicle is first in the line/ last in the line. What position is the red car? What type of vehicle is fourth?

Group activities

1   Show the children a necklace made of beads and ask questions about it. What colour is the first bead? What colour is the last bead? What position is the square bead? Ask the children to take six beads each and make a necklace. Children then need to describe their necklace, saying what colour bead is first, second, and so on.

2   Give children a blank number grid (3 x 3). Use one set of dot cards (shuffled). Children take turns to turn over a card and count the dots. Write the number in the grid. If a child has already written that number, the card is put to the bottom of the pile, and the next child turns over a card. Continue until one child has nine different numbers in their grid. Ask the remaining children to suggest numbers to write in their empty grids.

3   Give children two dice with dots on (one labelled one to six, the other die the same but cover the five and six and mark zero). Children roll the dice and count the dots, then write the total. (Some children may need to work with one die.)

Plenary

Discuss activity 1. Write the appropriate day on the board. Can the children identify the first letter, the third letter, the last letter, and so on?

Session 4:

Resources:
Set of ordinal number cards (1st, 2nd, 3rd, and so on)
Paper and coloured crayons (red, yellow and blue)
Selection of toy farm animals
Strips of squared paper

Starter

Children show all ten fingers and count on in tens, flashing fingers as they count. Count back in tens from 100. Say: 'Show me five!' Children hold up one hand. Now you hold up one hand and ask how many fingers they can see. Five. Continue: 'We are going to find out different ways of making five. Let's count how many fingers are standing up.' Five. 'How many are folded down?' Zero. Record this:

$$5 + 0 = 5$$

Fold down one finger. 'How many fingers are standing up?' Four. Children show four fingers up and one folded down. Record this:

$$4 + 1 = 5$$

Repeat until all five fingers are folded down:

$$0 + 5 = 5$$

Main teaching activity

Ask a group of eight children to line up. Who is first in the line? Who is last in the line? Who is third? Who is sixth? How can they work it out? Start by counting first, second, third, and so on. Give each child in the line an ordinal number card. Count again, pointing to the cards. Where else have the children seen numbers like this? When we write the date. Choose a different group of children and distribute the ordinal number cards amongst them. The cards tell them what position to be in. Can the children arrange themselves in the correct order?

Group activities

1   Ask children to write their names onto a piece of card/paper. Each child counts the number of letters in their name. Point to the first letter. Point to the last letter. Using a green crayon, draw a circle around the first letter. Using a blue crayon, draw a circle around the last letter. Choose a different colour and draw around the fourth letter. This may give a point for discussion, as some children may have circled it as their last letter.

2   Working with a partner, one child arranges six farm animals in a row. Their partner shouldn't see the row. By asking questions about the animals' position, their partner has to replicate the row.

3   Children have strips of squared paper and colour eight squares using only three colours (red, yellow and blue).

Plenary

Refer to the strips of paper from activity 3, asking questions, for example 'Stand up if you coloured your first square blue', 'Stay standing if you coloured your last square red'. Compare similarities and differences between patterns.

Session 5:

Resources:
Whiteboards for each child
Blank number lines and tracks (photocopiable sheet 7)
Large numeral cards (one to ten)
Numeral cards (zero to ten)
Paint and paper for finger painting

Starter

Children sit in a circle. Count up to 30 and beyond. Count around the circle in ones up to 20. Begin to count around the circle in ones but stop the count when you reach five. Can the children work out who will say number eight? Check by counting on. Were they correct? Continue the count from eight. Who will say the number 13? Continue from 13. Who will say 17? Repeat starting at zero again.

Main teaching activity

Draw a number line on the board. Children draw their own number lines on whiteboards. Mark where numbers three and six will go. Children write numbers three and six on their boards. Ask a child to identify where one will go. Ask the child to write one on the board. All the children then write one on their own whiteboard in the correct position. Can all the children write or have a go at writing number four in the correct place? How did they know where to put number four? Continue until the number line is complete.

Group activities

1   Give children a blank number line. Count the spaces. There are 11. Shuffle the set of large numeral cards one to ten. Ask the children to write zero in the first square. Explain that you are going to turn over a card and say the number. They have to find the right square to write that number in.

2   Working with a partner, each child has a blank number track. Shuffle a set of numeral cards (zero to ten) Children take it in turns to turn over a numeral card and say the number. They write the number down on the number track until they have completed the track.

3   Make numbers by finger painting. (Concentrate on this week's numbers.)

Plenary

Discuss activities 1 and 2.

Counting, adding and subtracting

Unit 8

Objectives:

Count in twos

Select two groups of objects to make a given total

Separate (partition) a given number of objects into two groups

Begin to find how many have been removed from a group of objects by counting up from a number

Vocabulary:

numbers zero to 100, counting in ones, counting in twos, count up from

How many?, add, total, altogether, makes

forwards, back from, begin at, stop at, different, separate, record, there were, there are, How many more?, Are there enough?, jump back, count back

References:

National Numeracy Strategy pages 2-10, 14-17

Curriculum Guidance for the Foundation Stage pages 68, 74-77

Note

Unit 8 consists of seven sessions. This is to enable the consolidation of counting on and counting back. These skills are important in developing a solid foundation in numeracy. Unit 9 has been adjusted to include only three sessions to allow for this.

Session 1:

Resources:

Tom Thumb's Musical Maths (A & C Black)
Large numeral cards (zero to 20)
Cubes for towers
Strips of squared paper and crayons

Starter

Starting at zero, count in ones up to 100 if possible. Count in tens up to 100 and back. Begin counting at 20 and then stop at 50. Begin at 40 and stop at 60. Begin at 30 and stop at 70. Sing 'Centipede and millipede' from *Tom Thumb's Musical Maths*.

Main teaching activity

Explain that today they are going to learn how to count in twos. Use rhymes/songs to help you, for example, 'The animals went in two by two' or 'Two, four, six, eight, Mary at the cottage gate'. First, count together in ones starting at number one and finishing at 20. Start by saying one quietly, two in a normal voice, three quietly, and so on, until number 20 is reached. Count again, but this time use numeral cards and point to the even numbers.

Group activities

1   Children make towers of two cubes. Explain that you are going to put all the towers together to make one big tower then count how many cubes you have altogether. Instead of counting in ones, they can count in twos. Count the cubes. Break off two cubes. Count how many are in the tower now.

2   Make a staircase of cubes, using steps of two.

3   Give the children strips of squared paper and ask them to colour the squares in blocks of two.

Plenary

Count in twos up to 20. Use the staircase and count in twos. Ask seven children to stand up. Count how many eyes one child has. Two. 'How many eyes have these children got altogether? Do we have to count each one? No, we can count in twos.'

Session 2:

Resources:
Nine skittles and a ball
Cubes for towers
Seven play food biscuits (or circles of card) and two plates

Starter

Children sit in a circle and count in ones up to 30. Count around the circle in ones up to 20. Tell the children that you want them to begin counting at number three and stop at nine. Start at seven and stop at 11. Start at five and stop at ten. Start at 12 and stop at 17. Progress to asking individual children to begin counting at a small number and finish at a given number.

Main teaching activity

Tell the children that you are going to find different ways of separating a group of objects into two groups. Stand nine skittles up. Ask a child to use a ball and try to knock down some skittles. Count how many skittles are knocked down and how many are still standing up. Record it, for example five down and four up would be: $5 + 4 = 9$

Repeat this several times. It is important to emphasise that there are nine skittles altogether each time.

Group activities

1   Make a tower of ten. (Depending on the children's ability, you may want to use less cubes.) Investigate the ways in which the tower can be broken into two groups. Children record their findings as number sentences.

2   Give the children seven play food biscuits (circles of card will be enough).

How many different ways can they put the seven biscuits on two plates? Children can record their results pictorially or as a number sentence.

3   Children play skittles, recording the results on a sheet of paper folded in half with headings 'down' and 'up'.

Plenary

Discuss today's activities.

Session 3:

Resources:
Number line
Small box (or bus outline) and play people
Egg boxes – one per child (activity 1) and different coloured plastic eggs or cubes
Different coloured cubes
Squared paper and coloured crayons
Toy farm animals

Starter

Say a number, for example 'four' and ask children to count on three. Tell them to put number four in their head and count 'five, six, seven' (unfurling fingers as each number is said). You may wish to use a number line to demonstrate, marking four on the line and counting on three spaces.

Main teaching activity

Tell the children that you are going to choose two groups of objects to make a given total. You will need a small box (or bus outline) and some play people. Only eight people can go on the bus. How many girls, how many boys? Seven boys and one girl. Write this as a number sentence: $7 + 1 = 8$

Ask another child to put eight people in the bus. Record how many girls and how many boys.

Group activities

1   Give children an egg box each. (If you don't have two different coloured plastic eggs use card or cubes.) Investigate and record the different ways of making six, for example four blue and two white.

2   Give children two different coloured cubes. How many different ways can they make seven. Children record their solutions using coloured crayons on squared paper.

3   Children choose two types of farm animals. How many different ways can they be combined in one field so that there is just a total of eight?

Plenary

Talk about the variety of solutions to today's activities.

Session 4:

Resources:
Number line

Dice

3 x 2 grids

Board games

Starter

Children sit in a circle and count up to ten and back. Count up to 20 and back around the circle. Say number seven and add three (tap your head as you say seven and use fingers to keep count as you count on). Say 'Seven add three makes ten'. Model by writing this as a number sentence: 7 + 3 = 10

Repeat, starting at five and counting on two. 'Five and two more makes seven.' Use the number line to demonstrate counting on.

Main teaching activity

Explain that you are going to roll two dice and keep a tally of the total scores. List the numbers two to 12. Roll the first die and say the number, for example three. Ask a child to roll the die and say the number, for example two. Encourage the children to put the number three in their head and count on two: 'Three and two more makes five'. Put a tally mark against five. Let the children take turns to roll the dice to establish the two numbers that are going to be added. Continue until ten tally marks are on the chart.

Group activities

1   Give each child a 3 x 2 grid. Roll two dice and work out the total. (Some children may need to count each dot individually.) Write the total in one square of the grid. Children take turns in rolling the dice. Repeat until all six squares are full.

2   Play board games such as snakes and ladders.

3   Use two dice and find different ways of making eight. Record by writing the two numbers or drawing dots.

Plenary

Use the grids made in activity 1 to play bingo. Roll two dice. Find the total. If the children have that total they cross the number out.

Session 5:

Resources:
Number lines and counters for each child (You may want to use sweets or other objects to support the main teaching activity.)

Cubes for towers

Dice numbered 0, 1, 1, 2, 2, 3

Sand tray

Numbered carpet tiles

Starter

Say to the children: 'Show me four fingers! Shake your fingers. Now show me three fingers!' Repeat several times. Then explain that you are going to use both hands to add two numbers together. 'Show me three fingers on one hand and two fingers on the other hand. How many fingers are there altogether?' As each finger is counted, encourage the children to touch their chin or nose with that finger. Count up to 20, starting at zero, and back.

Main teaching activity

The children need to be quite confident at counting back for this activity. They are going to find out how many are left when some are taken away. Ask: 'I had five sweets, I ate two of them. How many sweets have I got left?' Show how to count back two from five, putting five in your head and then saying 'four, three', keeping count by unfolding one finger as each number is said. Say: 'Five take away two is three'. Record this as a number sentence: 5 – 2 = 3 Repeat using different numbers of objects.

Group activities

1   Using a number line, start at ten and count back to zero. Find seven, put a counter on the square. Count back three. (Make sure children don't count the starting point as the first jump.) 'What number have you landed on?' Write the number sentence 7 - 3 = 4. Repeat with different size steps back and starting points.

2   Working with a partner, children make a tower of ten cubes each. They roll the die, break off the number of cubes shown, and count back as each cube is removed. The first person to have no cubes left is the winner.

3   Give each child five cubes (one colour per child). Children take it in turns to roll the die and bury that amount of cubes in the sand tray, until all of their cubes are buried. Then play in reverse, rolling the die and digging up the buried cubes. The winner is the person who buries and retrieves all five cubes.

Plenary

Arrange the carpet tiles as a number line. A child stands in square five. 'If he takes two steps back, what square will he be in?' Ask children to count back. Say 'five' as you tap your head, 'four' (unfurl one finger), 'three' (unfurl second finger). Get the child to step back two squares. 'We said five count back two is three. What square are you standing in? Number three.' Repeat using different starting points and steps back.

Session 6:

Resources:
Plate of biscuits (play food or card circles)
Objects for solving problems and to hide - buttons, toy animals
Small box or bag
Cubes made into towers
Sand tray

Starter

Count up to 50 and beyond in ones. 'Show me ten!' Children hold up two hands. You hold up both hands. 'How many fingers can you see?' Ten. 'We are going to find out different ways of making ten. Let's count how many fingers are standing up.' Ten. 'How many are folded down?' None – or zero. Record this: $10 + 0 = 10$ Fold down one finger. 'How many fingers are standing up?' Nine. The children show nine fingers up and one folded down. Record this: $9 + 1 = 10$ Repeat until all ten fingers are folded down.

Main teaching activity

Today the children are going to find out how many have been removed by counting up to the larger number. Show the children a plate with five biscuits on. Explain: 'There were seven biscuits on my plate. There are only five there now. How many have been eaten?' Can the children suggest ways of finding out? 'Let's put five in our head.' (Touch your head as the number five is said. As six is said, hold up one finger, say seven and hold up another finger. Point to the plate and say 'Five and two makes seven'. Ask children to solve other problems using the same method, for example: 'I had six pencils in my pot. There are only two now. How many have I lost?' 'There were eight buttons on my coat. There are only five now. How many have fallen off?'

Group activities

1   Use a small box and count out seven objects (small bears, elephants). 'How many bears have we got?' Seven. Ask children to close their eyes while you put four in the box. Ask: 'How many bears can you see?' Three. 'Let's work out how many are in the box. How many bears were there altogether?' Seven. 'Start at three and count up to seven. Four are in the bag.

2   Give children an assortment of cubes made into small towers - there should be ten in each tower. They need to work out how many more cubes are needed to make ten. They can write the number of cubes they have and then draw the additional cubes needed.

3   Hide some items in the sand tray and display the remainder nearby on separate sheets of paper which tell the children how many items there are altogether. For example, there are two cars on the paper and the number seven. The children have to work out how many cards are buried in the sand and write it down. They uncover the toys and check their answer.

Plenary

Discuss today's activities.

Session 7:

Resources:
Large numeral cards
Rabbit cards (photocopiable sheet 13)
Small box/bag and objects for counting
Counters
Sand tray and items to bury

Starter

Spread the large numeral cards out on the floor, face down, randomly. Ask the children to pick four cards and identify the numbers. Can the children order the numbers, starting with the largest number? Can they say what numbers are missing? Children then pick another four cards and repeat the process.

Main teaching activity

This session reinforces and extends yesterday's session. Explain that today you are going to find out how many have been removed by counting up. Using the rabbit cards, count out seven rabbits. 'There are seven rabbits. They are going to play hide and seek.' Ask the children to close their eyes while you remove three. 'How many rabbits are left?' Four. 'Let's work out how many are hiding. Put four in your head and count up to seven.' Say 'four and three makes seven, seven take away three makes four'. Count out eight rabbits. Children close their eyes while five rabbits hide. Repeat the above process.

Group activities

1   As for session 6.

2   Children work with a partner. One child picks an amount of counters, for example six, and gives them to their partner who then covers some of them with their hand. The child has to work out how many are covered by counting on until the required number is reached.

3   As for session 6.

Plenary

Discuss activities 2 and 3.

Shape, space and reasoning

Unit 9

Objectives:

Use everyday words to describe position, direction and movement

Sort and match objects, shapes and pictures, justifying the decisions made

Solve simple problems in a practical context. What could we try next?

Vocabulary:

numbers zero to 100, count in ones

up, down, through, turn, corner, forwards, backwards, left, right, position, above, below, along, direction, in the middle, next to, curved, straight, more than, less than, instructions, maze, different, find

What if ...?, How many different ways? What could we try next?

References:

National Numeracy Strategy pages 18-19, 24-27

Curriculum Guidance for the Foundation Stage pages 69, 80-81

Session 1:

Resources:

Large numeral cards (zero to 20) and washing line

A toy

Construction toys/Lego bricks and a toy car

Playmat (with road design) or create a road layout outside

Objects to hide

Starter

Count in ones to 50 and beyond, then tell the children that you are going to play a game called 'What's my number?' Children have to guess the numeral card that you are holding. They have to ask questions to find out what the number is. You can answer 'yes' or 'no'. (If you have another adult working with you, model the questions.) Use the washing line as a visual aid. For example: 'Is your number more than five?' 'No.' Turn over all the numeral cards more than five so that no numbers are showing and the children can see only the numbers that they could choose. 'Is your number less than two?' 'No.' 'Has your number got curved lines?' 'No.' You are left with the number four. At first, the questions from the children will be very simplistic, for example 'Is the number seven?' Gradually, with repetition, children will develop their questioning skills.

Main teaching activity

The whole group sits in a circle. Ask everyone if they were somewhere in the dark, and tried to walk out of the room, what might happen? Refer to the Roamer or a remote control car. You have to give it instructions so that it knows where to go. Put a toy in the centre of the group and ask a child to go and pick it up. Next time, blindfold a child and ask the others to give directions on how to get to the toy, for example, 'Take two steps forward and stop. Turn around, and so on.'

Group activities

1   Take children on a walk around school. Look at key points, for example where you need to turn corners, and so on. Which way do you turn? You can suggest ways to record these directions. (You will be using the information from today's walk in tomorrow's lesson.)

2   Construct a simple maze using construction toys and Lego. The children are going to give instructions to another child or adult to enable them to move a toy car through the maze.

3   Children use a playmat (road design) or design your own outside for children to use with toy vehicles.

Plenary

Hide an object in the classroom. Give simple instructions on how to find it. Ask two children to direct a child to get something, such as a pencil.

Session 2:

Resources:
Lego/building bricks and play person
Construction toys

Starter

Draw a large blank number line on the board. Write zero at one end and ten at the other. Invite a child to write the number one in the correct place. Ask them to explain how they worked it out. Ask another child to write number nine. Discuss how they worked out where to write it. Write number five on the line. Ask other children to write the remaining numbers on the number line, getting them to explain their choice of position.

Main teaching activity

We need directions to tell us how to get somewhere. Use key vocabulary - forward, turning a corner, going straight, backwards, turning left/right. Give children a point within the classroom to focus on and then begin to ask the children for directions on how to reach the area. Several children may give different directions depending upon the route taken around an obstacle, such as a table. As the children give directions, record them as a series of arrows. Refer to yesterday's walk around the school.

1   Before the session, build a maze using Lego or building bricks. Ask children to give directions for moving a play person through the maze from start to finish.

2   Working with an adult, children make a plan of the classroom and draw key features on it, such as tables, sand tray, floor cushions, graphic area and so on.

3   Children make a maze using Lego or building bricks.

Plenary

Use the plan made in activity 2 to discuss the route around the classroom.

Session 3:

Resources:
Cubes for towers
Coloured chalk or markers
2-d shapes
Squared paper
Old birthday/Christmas cards or patterned paper plates
Paper and glue

Starter

Today children are going to find different ways of making five. They can use a tower of five cubes. Say a number, for example three. Children break off three cubes and count the remainder. 'Three and two makes five.' Put the tower back together. Say the number four. Children break off four: 'Four and one makes five'.

Main teaching activity

Draw several outlines of a scarf on the board. Each scarf is going to have three stripes. Show the children three colours that they can use to draw the stripes. What if all the stripes are the same colour? What can you change if you keep the middle colour the same?

Group activities

1   Show the children three different 2-d shapes arranged in a line. Record the arrangement. Give the children three 2-d shapes and ask them to copy the original arrangement. Ask them to move their three shapes around into a different order. Record their patterns.

2   Children use cubes (two colours). How many different ways can they make a tower of three cubes? Children can record their solutions on squared paper.

3   Ask children to cut up some old birthday/Christmas cards or patterned paper plates into four or five pieces. Mix up the pieces. Can they stick them onto a piece of paper to recreate the original picture?

Plenary

Discuss today's activities. See if the children can suggest a strategy for finding the possible combinations.

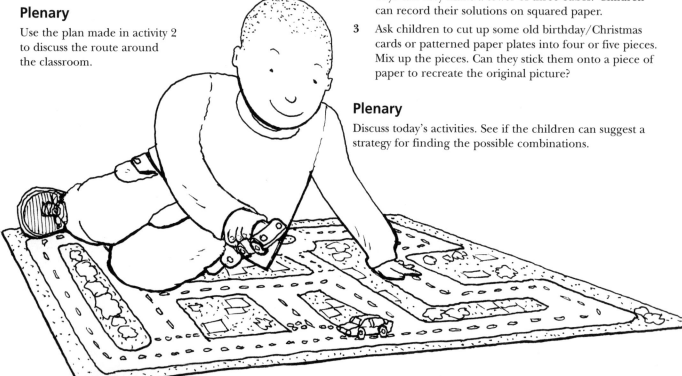

Counting, numbers and measures

Unit 10

Objectives:

Begin to write numerals to 20

Estimate a number beyond ten and check by counting

Begin to read o' clock time

Vocabulary:

How many?, count, numbers up to 50 and beyond, guess, estimate, write, check, next number, correct order, more than, less than

clock, time, day, week, hour, o'clock, before, after, today, yesterday, day, night, days of the week, takes longer, long/short hand, around

References:

Counting, reading and writing numbers *National Numeracy Strategy* pages 2-10

Measures including time *National Numeracy Strategy* pages 22-23

Curriculum Guidance for the Foundation Stage pages 68-70, 74-75, 80-81

Session 1:

Resources:
Numeral cards (zero to nine) – one set per child
Large analogue clock
Large circular piece of paper
Numbers one to 12 written onto card
Long and short hand made from card
Small clocks
Numeral cards one to 12 (activity 2)
Strips of paper
Sand timer

Starter

Children all have their own set of numeral cards and arrange them in the correct order. Say a number and the children hold up the corresponding card. Repeat several times. 'Show me a number that is one more than three.' Repeat using 'one more' several times, then introduce 'one less than'. If children are finding it difficult, refer to the number line and demonstrate that

less $\longleftarrow$———————————————————$\longrightarrow$ more

Main teaching activity

Sing 'Hickory, Dickory Dock'. Show the children an analogue clock. What do we use a clock for? To tell the time. Name the parts of the clock. Look at the two hands, the long and short hand. What numbers can they see on the clock? Use a large circular piece of paper and numbers one to 12 on pieces of card. Ask the children to put the number cards onto the piece of paper in the correct order. Use the clock to show how the long hand goes around the clock face once, yet the short hand just moves to the next number. Show the children the long and short hand made of card. Attach them to the circle of paper to tell the time of 1 o'clock. Explain that when the long hand points to the 12, the time is ___o'clock

1   Give children a small clock each. You use a large clock. Tell the children you are going to make 1 o'clock. Move the long hand to the 12, and the short hand to the one. The children then make 1 o' clock with their clock. Continue modelling various o' clock times, the children copying you. Ask the children to make 3 o'clock. You make 3 o'clock and see if their clocks match. Continue, getting children to make more o' clock times.

2   Children use numeral cards to order the numbers one to 12. Write numbers one to 12 on a strip of paper. (Keep for the following day, to make a clock face).

3   Use a sand timer to time one minute. Choose an activity, for example how many beads can you thread in one minute? How many times can you write your name? How many cubes can you put together in a tower? Record the outcome by writing the number or using tally marks.

Plenary

Discuss activity 3.

Session 2:

Resources:
Cubes for towers
The Bad Tempered Ladybird by Eric Carle (Puffin)
Large clock
Clocks used in session 1
Paper plates, long and short hands, and paper fasteners
Sand timer

Starter

Give each child a tower of five cubes. Say a number, for example three. Children break off three cubes and count the remainder. 'Three and two makes five.' Put the tower back together. Say the number four. Children break off four cubes. 'Four and one makes five.'

Main teaching activity

Read *The Bad Tempered Ladybird* by Eric Carle. Discuss the time the ladybird meets the other animals. Using a large clock, let children create the o'clock times referred to in the story.

Group activities

1   As for session 1 but focus on the children making their own o'clock times.

2   Use a paper plate as a clock face. Cut the numbers from yesterday and arrange to form the clock face. Attach a long and short hand to the plate with a paper fastener. Children choose what o' clock time they want to make

3   As for session 1.

Plenary

Children show the time on their own clock. Identify important times of the day for them, for example 7 o'clock they get up, 9 o'clock they come to school, 12 o'clock is lunchtime, 3 o'clock is home time, and so on.

Session 3:

Resources:
Clock faces (paper plates) with o' clock times drawn on
Washing line
Small clocks
Paper, paint or crayons
Materials for class display or book

Starter

Play 'What's my number?' as in Unit 9, session 1.

Main teaching activity

Show the children o' clock times. The children tell you what hour the short hand is pointing to, for example three, so it is 3 o' clock. What happens at 3 o'clock? Once all the times have been identified, the children can sequence all the clocks on the washing line, starting with 1 o'clock.

Group activities

1   Each child has their own clock. Ask the children to make a time, for example 4 o'clock. Once the children are comfortable doing this, ask them to make the time that they get up. What time do they have lunch?

2   Children paint or draw a picture to go with the o'clock time they made yesterday. Make a class display or book. Arrange the pictures in chronological order.

3   Sequence the clocks on the washing line.

Plenary

Discuss activity 2.

Session 4:

Resources:

Cubes for towers

Dot cards or pictures from a counting frieze

Counters

Large numeral cards

3 x 3 grids

Small containers with small objects inside

Starter

Children can use a tower of ten cubes. Say a number, for example three. Children break off three and count the remainder. 'Three and seven makes ten.' Put the tower back together. Say the number four. Children break off four. 'Four and six makes ten.'

Main teaching activity

By now children should be gaining confidence in estimating using small numbers. Begin by using dot cards or pictures from a counting frieze. Show the dots/pictures for a few seconds before asking the children for an estimate. (Don't give the children time to count.) Then take a collection of counters and spread them out on the floor so that every counter can be seen (extend the numbers up to and beyond 20.) Then count them. Repeat this activity but try putting the counters close together or scattering them. Which is easier to estimate?

Group activities

1   Children are introduced to writing numbers beyond ten, if appropriate. Ensure that they understand they are writing one ten and one more when they write 11, one ten and two more when they write 12 - it helps reduce digit reversal and begins to introduce the important element of place value. Spread large numeral cards face down on the table. Children turn over a card, identify the number and then write it.

2   Give each child a 3 x 3 grid. They write nine numbers, one in each square, and use the grid to play bingo with an additional adult.

3   Give children small containers with small objects in. They estimate how many objects are in the container, then check by counting.

Plenary

Using a large blank number line, mark zero at one end and ten at the other. Ask children to write in the missing numbers. What number is after ten? Eleven. Ask a child to write the number on the line. What number will come next? Continue until 20 is reached. Count from zero to 20, pointing to the numbers as they are said.

Session 5:

Resources:

Large numeral cards and washing line

Three transparent containers and beads

Variety of containers (yoghurt pots, matchboxes) and objects to fit inside

Paper and drawing materials

A big book

Starter

Children put large numeral cards on the washing line in the correct order. They then close their eyes while you take a couple of cards and change their position. The children identify what has been changed. Repeat the activity, gradually increasing the amount of cards that are being exchanged.

Main teaching activity

Using three transparent containers put different amounts of beads in each one. Can the children identify which pot contains the least? Children estimate the amount. Empty them out onto a tray. Do any of them want to change their estimate? Count how many there were. Was it easier to estimate when the beads were in the container or on the tray? Ask a child to pick another container and estimate the number of beads. (You will probably have to scaffold some children's answers by suggesting possible limits. Do they think there are more than 30? Remind the children how many were in the previous container. Prompt them to use appropriate language, for example 'more than', 'less than'.)

Group activities

1   Show the children a variety of containers. Ask the children to guess how many objects will fit into a specific container, for example 'How many Lego bricks will fit into a yoghurt pot?' Children offer their estimates and then check them. How many 1p coins can you get in a matchbox? Children offer their estimates and then check by counting.

2   Children choose a book. Set a page number, for example page 9. They open the book, estimate the number of words on the page and write their estimate down. Then children count the words. Record their answer in red on the same piece of paper.

3   Children write or paint a number then put the corresponding pictures to match the number.

Plenary

Discuss activities 1 and 2. Use a big book. Ask a child to say a page number then ask another child to find the correct page. The children estimate how many words are on the page then count them.

Counting, adding, subtracting and money

Unit 11

Objectives:

Count in tens

Count beyond 20 in twos

Use numerals to record numbers

Work out by counting how many more are needed to make a larger number

Use coins in role play to pay and give change

Vocabulary:

numbers up to 100

count in ones, twos and tens

coin, pence, buy, cost, spend, combine, price, pay, change, left

count up, count back, worth most/least

How many more?, and, add, more, makes, altogether

References:

Counting, reading and writing numbers *National Numeracy Strategy* pages 2-10

Adding and subtracting *National Numeracy Strategy* pages 14-17

Money and real life problems *National Numeracy Strategy* pages 20-21

Curriculum Guidance for the Foundation Stage pages 68-69, 74-77

Session 1:

Resources:

1p, 2p, 5p, 10p and 20p coin for each child

Flat tray

Five 1p coins

Selection of coins for group activities

Labels

Starter

Children sit in a circle and count in tens up to 100 and back, flashing fingers as in Unit 5. Start at 30. Can the children continue the count? Use other starting points, such as 50, and count around the circle in tens. Count back in tens around the circle.

Main teaching activity

Give each child a 1p, 2p, 5p, 10p and 20p coin. Play a version of 'Show me': 'Show me 5p'. 'Show me 10p.' 'Show me a coin worth less than 5p/more than 5p.' Put a selection of coins including five 1p coins on a flat tray. Explain that everyone is going to sing 'Five currant buns in the baker's shop'. When you choose someone to buy a bun they have to come and get their 1p from the tray. Sing 'Five currant buns'. Ask the children, if you wanted to buy two buns, how much would it cost? If each bun cost 3p how much would two buns cost? If one bun cost 1p, and a cake cost 2p, how much would they need to be able to buy them? Children should be encouraged to count on (they may need a number line to help them).

Group activities

1   Each child has a selection of coins - 1ps, 2ps and 5ps, depending on the group of children. Choose two items from the shop. How much do they cost altogether? Scribe 2p + 3p. Can the children make the two amounts, combine the coins, then count them to give the total, 5p. If they had worked out the total first, would they have used a different coin? Choose two different items. Can the children record the two prices and the total, then select the appropriate coins to pay.

2   Children write price labels for the shop. Give the children specific coins, for example three 1ps. They write a label for 3p.

3   Children role play in the shop.

Plenary

Choose two price labels from activity 2. How much would these two items cost? Can the children work out the answer by counting on? Can they get the appropriate 1p coins? (If the total is 2p or 5p some children may choose the appropriate coin.)

Session 2:

Resources:

Large number line

Selection of coins up to £1 for main activity

Selection of coins for each child (activity 1)

Coin track game (photocopiable sheet 27)

Starter

Start at zero and count up to and back from 20. Children hold up five fingers. Say: 'Five take away three'. Fold down three fingers. How many are left? Encourage children to count back as they fold each finger down. Children show you how many are left. Point to the number line as you count back. Repeat several times using five as the larger number, before extending up to ten.

Main teaching activity

Familiarise the children with the coins up to 20p. Display them so all the children can see (peg large facsimile coins onto the washing line). Explain that you are going to put them in order depending on their value. Which coin is worth the least? Place it on the left. Which coin is worth the most? Place it on the right. Children complete the line. Show the children a 50p coin. Can a child suggest where this will go in the line? Why? Show them the £1 coin. Where will this go? Explain that £1 is worth 100 pennies.

Group activities

1   As for session 1.

2   Play the coin track game.

3   Shop play - can the children choose two items and record their purchases showing a total?

Plenary

Discuss activity 3. Explain that you want the children to look at their hand and count their five fingers. They can use their fingers to help find different ways of making five. Ask them to think of five 1p pieces. Can they find different ways of making 5p? Can they use this information to find two items that they can buy for 5p?

Session 3:

Resources:

Selection of coins (some with Blu-Tack attached ready to stick to board)

5p and 10p coins for each child (activity 1)

Items from the role-play shop with price labels

Price labels

Paper and wax crayons

Starter

Children sit in a circle. Say the rhyme 'Two, four, six, eight, Mary at the cottage gate'. Children count in twos up to 20. Ask them to stretch their legs out in front of them. Explain that you want to count how many legs all the class have. Count in twos. Ask a group of 11 children to stand up. Count how many legs. Ask a group of 12 children to stand up. Count how many eyes. Continue, varying the group of children and counting ears, shoes, and so on.

Main teaching activity

Put a 2p coin on the board. At the shop you want to buy a sweet. It costs 1p. How much change will you get? Encourage the children to use fingers or the number line to work out the answer. Put a 5p coin on the board. 'How much is this coin worth?' Five pence. 'I want to buy an apple. It costs three pence.' Ask children for ideas on what you can do. Explain that you need some change. Can they help you work out how much change you need? 'We are going to start counting at three and count up to five. Put three in your head.' Say 'four, five', using fingers to keep count. 'How much change do I need?' Two. 'Two what?' Two pence. Ask a child to get two pence. (I find that putting the apple and 2 pence together helps the children to visualise the process of giving change.) By changing the 5p coin for five 1p coins, you can demonstrate spending 3p and count how much is left. Repeat by taking 10p to the shop and spending 6p.

Group activities

1   Choose some items from the shop (not priced at 5p or 10p). Give each child a 5p or 10p coin. Ask them to choose an item from the shop, for example an item that costs 4p. The child then works out how much change they will need.

2   Give children some price labels. The children select appropriate coins to make that amount then, using a wax crayon, they place the coin (or coins) under the paper and rub over it with the crayon.

3   Shop play. Children should have the opportunity to buy/give change in the shop.

Plenary

Choose some price labels (activity 2) and discuss the coins that the children have chosen. Show the children a 10p coin. 'If I spend 7p (show the children a corresponding price label), how much change will I get?'

Session 4:

Resources:

Five toys

Plates, hats and other items for party

Variety of containers and selection of items to go inside

Coins

Role-play shop

Number track and counters

Starter

Count in ones to 30, saying one, three, five and so on quietly and two, four, six, and so on in a normal spoken voice. Then count in twos up to 30. Children hold up one finger on one hand and two on the other. How many fingers altogether? Encourage the children to begin to count on from two. Model the number sentence on the board: 2 + 2 = 4 Repeat using different amounts of fingers and modelling the number sentence. The children may be ready for you to write a number sentence on the board and they hold up the corresponding fingers and provide you with the answer. Invite a child to come and write the answer.

Main teaching activity

This concept can be quite difficult for children to grasp, so it is essential that the children see the practical application. Explain that five toys are going to have a party and you have bought some things for the party. Put the five toys in a line. Take four plates and put them in front of the toys. 'Oh dear! Something's wrong.' The children will tell you that not every toy has a plate. How many more plates do you need? 'I have got four.' Touch plate number four as you say four then hold up one finger as five is said. 'Four and one makes five. I need to get one more plate.' Repeat using this process for other items at the party.

Group activities

1   Use a blank number track at first. Ask the children to take three counters each and place one in each square. How many more counters are needed to make ten? The children count the number of empty spaces. Repeat the activity using different amounts of counters as a starting point. (Some children may benefit from using an egg box instead of a number track.) Ask questions, for example: 'How many counters have you got? How many do you need altogether? How many more do you need?'

2   Put a selection of items into a variety of containers. Give each container a target number, for example nine. Children count how many more items they will need to put into each container to make nine. They then write on small pieces of paper the amount of items needed and place it in the container. (You might want to give some children small targets no greater than five, or use a sorting tray.)

3   As for session 3.

Plenary

Discuss activity 2.

Session 5:

Resources:

Tower of tens cubes for each child

Two rabbit cards and house outlines numbered one to ten

5 x 4 grids, counters and a die

Pots of crayons and paper

Role-play shop and money

Starter

Start at zero and count up to 100. Children can use a tower of ten cubes. Say a number, for example five. Children break off five cubes and count the remainder. 'Five and five makes ten.' Put the tower back together. Say the number four. Children break off four and say 'Four and six makes ten'.

Main teaching activity

You need house outlines with doors numbered one to ten and two rabbit cards. Put one rabbit in house number three and the other in number seven. How many jumps does rabbit need to get to his friend? As you say 'one', make sure your finger is pointing to number four, at 'two' point to five and 'three' point to six. Say 'four' when you reach rabbit's house. 'Rabbit has to take four jumps.' Repeat using different start and finish points.

1   Give each child a 5 x 4 grid. Children take it in turns to roll a die and take the corresponding number of counters and put one in each square. As each child puts their counters on the grid, ask them how many counters they have and how many more they need to win. They need to roll the exact amount.

2   Give the children a pot of green crayons, a pot of blue crayons, a pot of yellow crayons, and so on, and a sheet of paper. You need eight crayons in each pot. Ask: 'How many more green crayons do I need to make eight?' They can use that coloured crayon to write the answer.

3   As for session 3.

Plenary

Discuss activity 2.

Assess and review

Unit 12

By the end of Unit 11 most children should be able to:

- Recite numbers beyond 20
- Count in tens
- Count in twos up to and then beyond 20

- Write numerals to ten and beyond
- Begin to understand and use ordinal numbers in different contexts

- Select two groups of objects to make a given total
- Separate (partition) a given number of objects into two groups
- Begin to find how many have been removed from a group of objects by counting up from a number
- Work out by counting how many more are needed to make a larger number

- Estimate a number up to ten and beyond
- Begin to solve simple problems in a practical context, respond to 'What could we try next?'

- Sort and match objects, shapes and pictures, justifying the decisions made
- Begin to read o'clock time
- Use everyday words to describe position, direction and movement

- Begin to buy and give change in play situations

Pages 13 to 15 of *Using Assess and Review Lessons* (DfES 0632/2001) provide examples of questions that can be used to assess a child's understanding against the key objectives.

Remember that the information these assessments provide must be used to plan the children's activities at the appropriate level. This may mean revisiting, consolidating or extending the level at which the child is working.

After these sessions you will be able to identify the children that have achieved the Foundation Stage Early Learning Goals. Some children upon reaching Year 1 will require further support to achieve this level. It is crucial that accurate recording of their achievements are handed on to their next teacher.

DOT CARDS

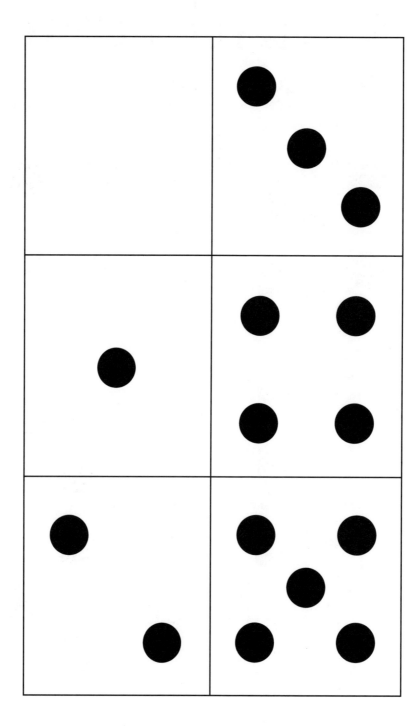

Note: Large dot cards are required for some activities – enlarge on a photocopier and laminate.

DOT CARDS

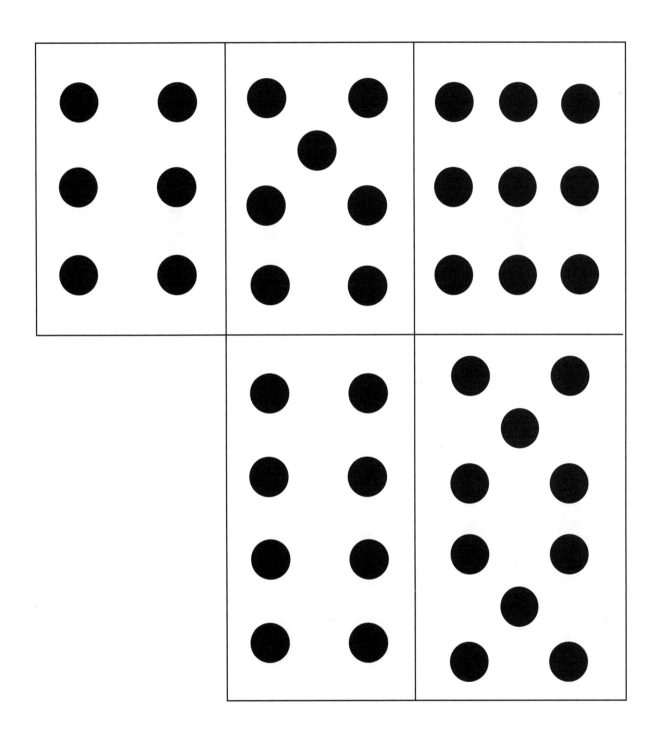

NUMERAL CARDS

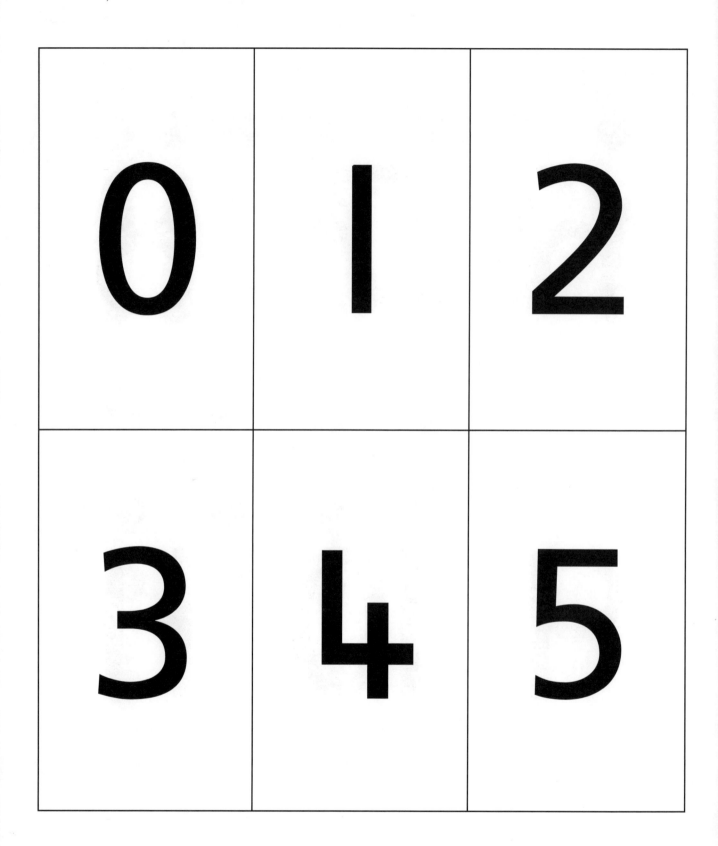

Note: Large numeral cards are required for some activities – enlarge on a photocopier and laminate.

NUMERAL CARDS

6	7	8
9	10	11

NUMERAL CARDS

| 12 | 13 | 14 |
| 15 | 16 | 17 |

NUMERAL CARDS

18	19	20

NUMBER LINES AND TRACKS

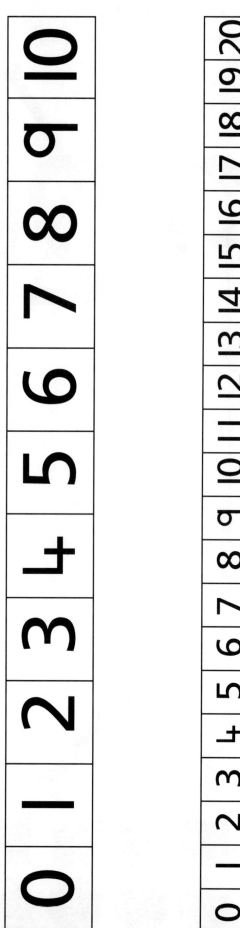

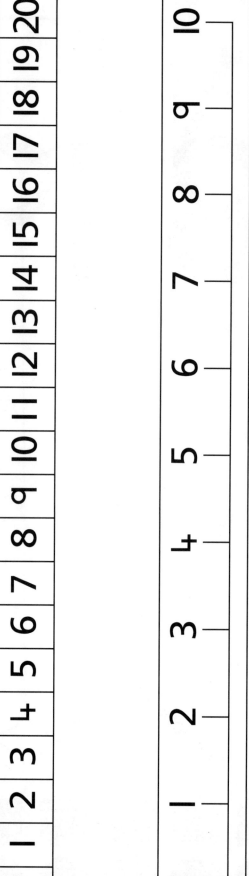

Note: Enlarge on a photocopier to A3 size. Cut out and laminate.

LADYBIRD

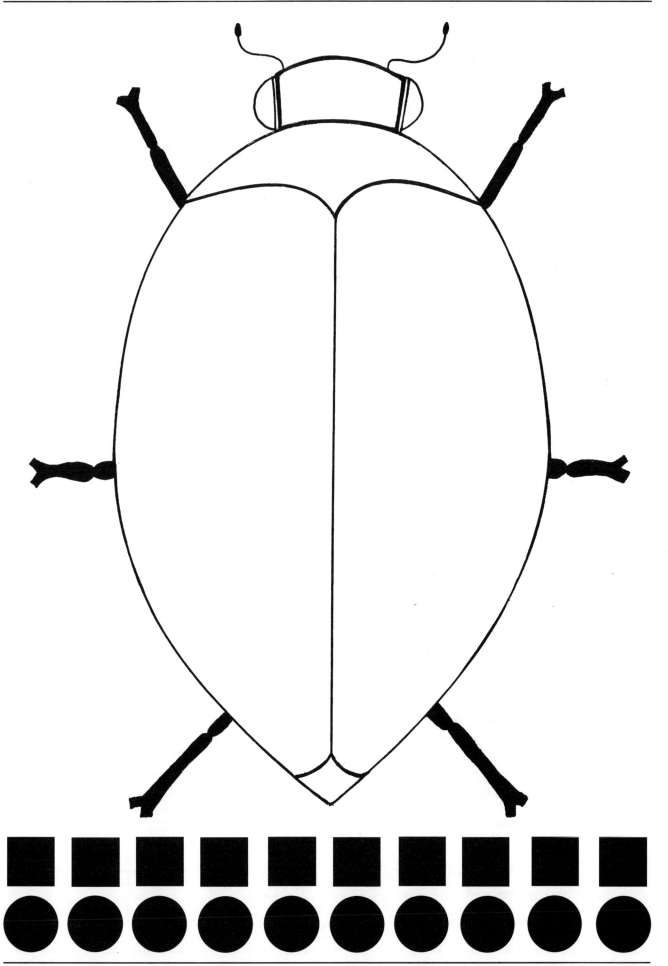

LADYBIRD CARDS

Instructions: photocopy two sheets for playing Pelmanism (pairs), snap or ordering.

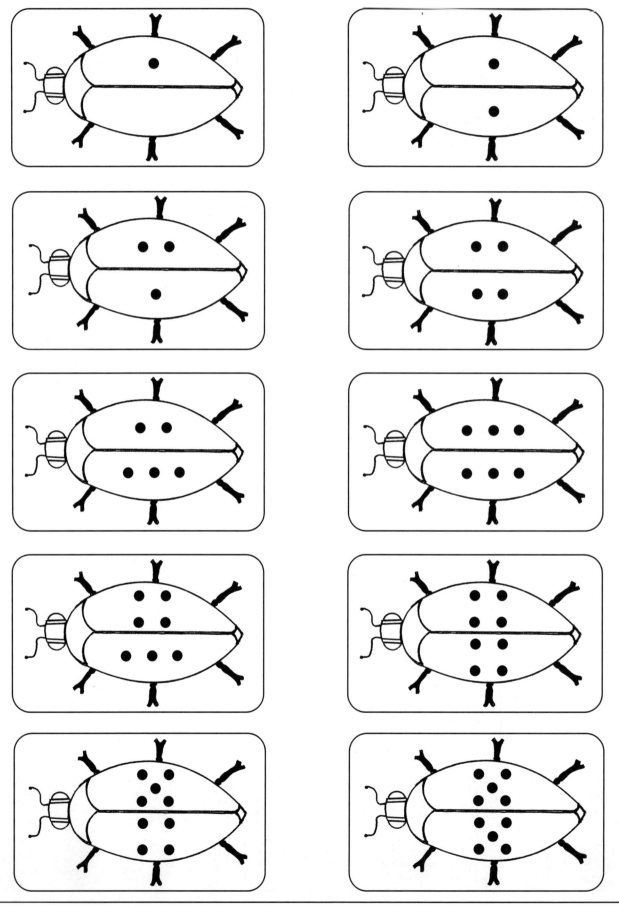

SHAPE LOTTO

Instructions: Make two copies of each card (enlarged if possible). Laminate one copy to use as the baseboard. Cut up the remainder to ensure you have enough matching shapes.

How to play shape lotto

Give each child a baseboard.

Shuffle the cut-out shapes and put them in a pile. Name the shapes that will be used: circle, square, triangle, rectangle.

Take the top card from the pile and ask a child to name it. Have they got this shape on their board? If they have, the child takes the card and covers the shape. Turn over the next card and ask the second child the same question. Repeat.

If a child has already covered the shape, put the card to the bottom of the pile and play passes to the next child.

The first child to cover all the shapes on their board is the winner.

SHAPE LOTTO

SHAPES

These shapes can be used to make repeating patterns as well as for identifying shapes. Enlarge them on a photocopier, colour, cut out and laminate or photocopy onto coloured paper/card.

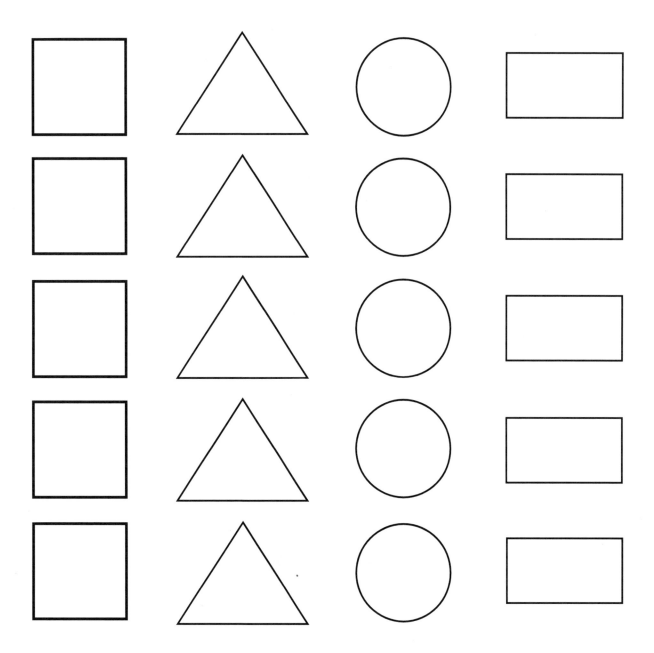

RABBIT CARDS

LONG AND SHORT SNAKES

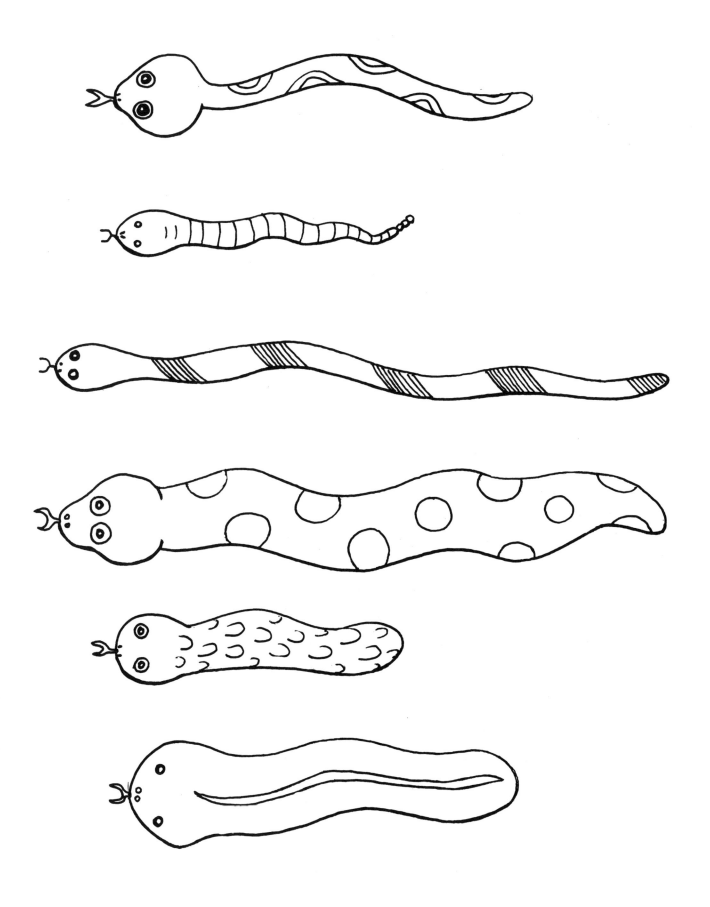

TEN IN THE BED

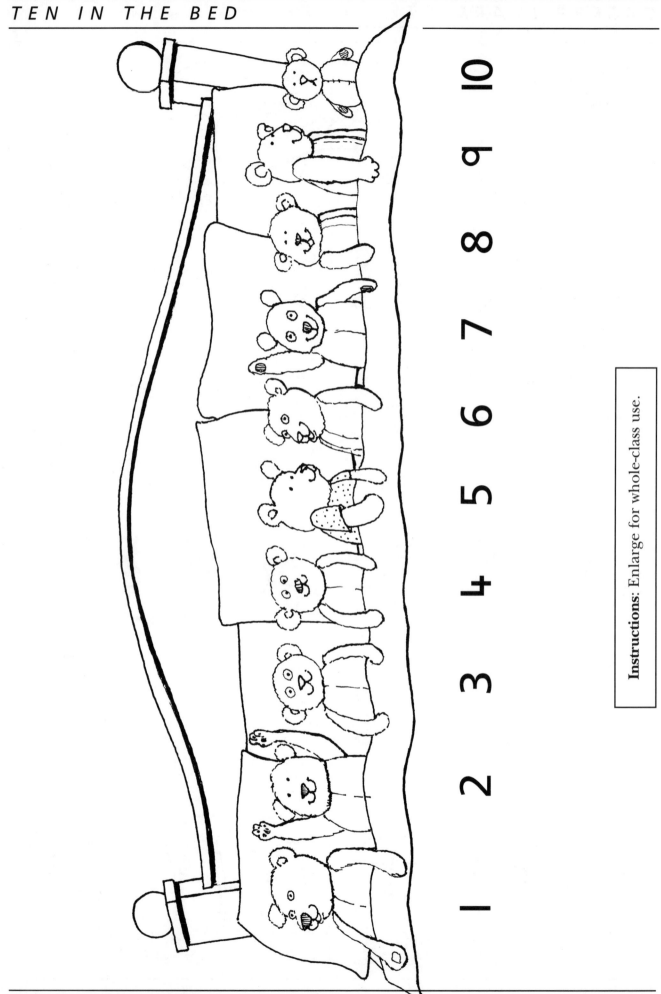

1 2 3 4 5 6 7 8 9 10

Instructions: Enlarge for whole-class use.

CATERPILLARS

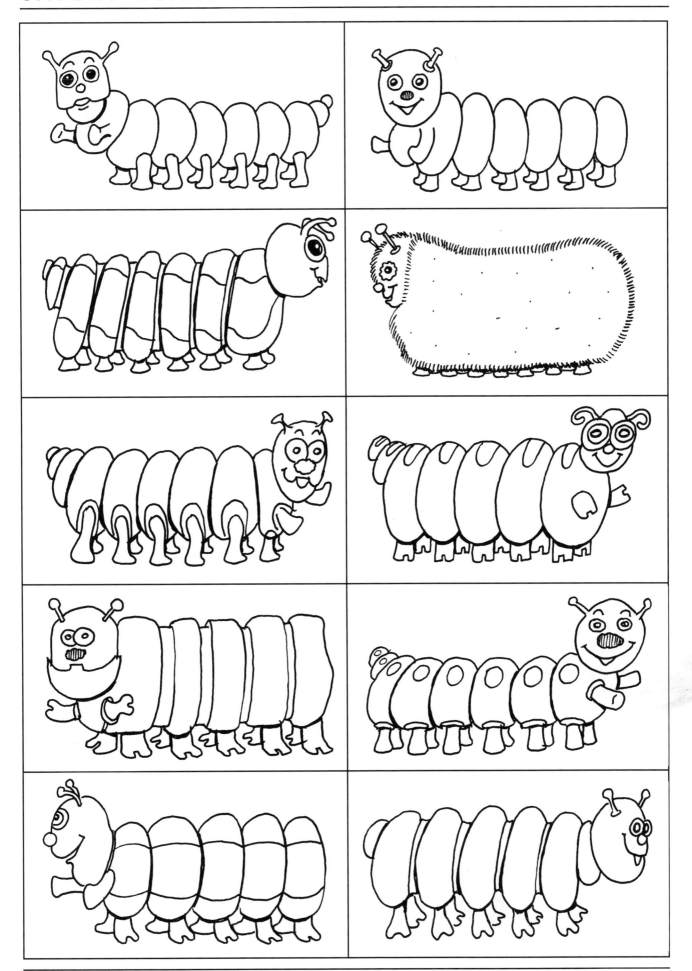

FIVE LITTLE DUCKS

Instructions: Enlarge the ducks for whole-class activity.

BUTTERFLIES

Instructions: Copy, cut out and cut in half for children to match.

WHERE DO THEY LIVE? (A)

WHERE DO THEY LIVE? (B)

MAKING SALT DOUGH

8 cups of flour

2 cups of salt

3 cups of water

BUS

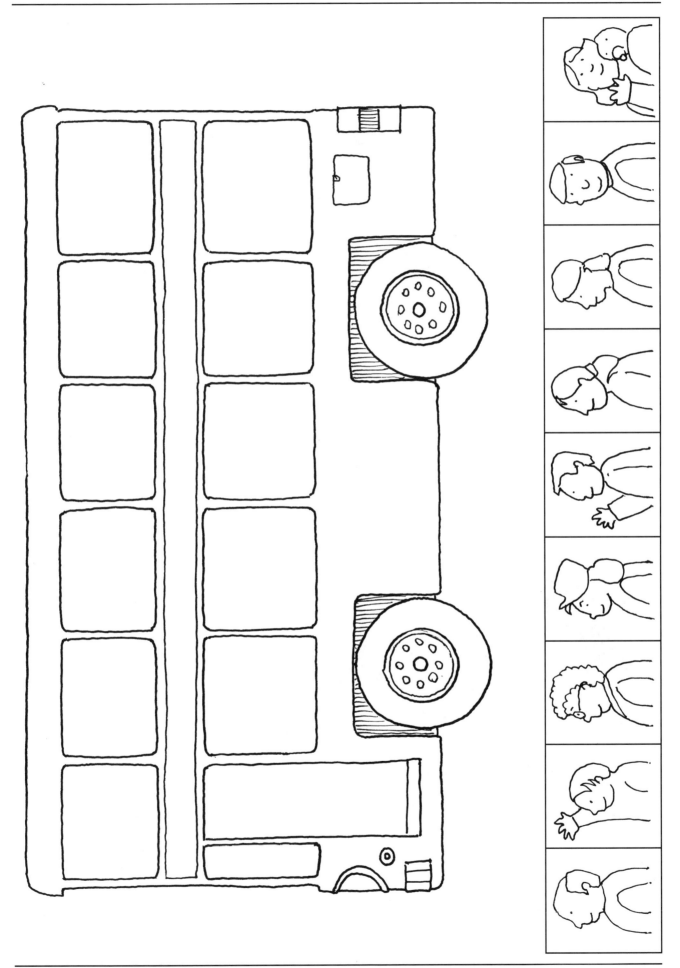

NUMBER TRACK

CAKES AND SWEETS

COINS

COLLECT 1P GAME

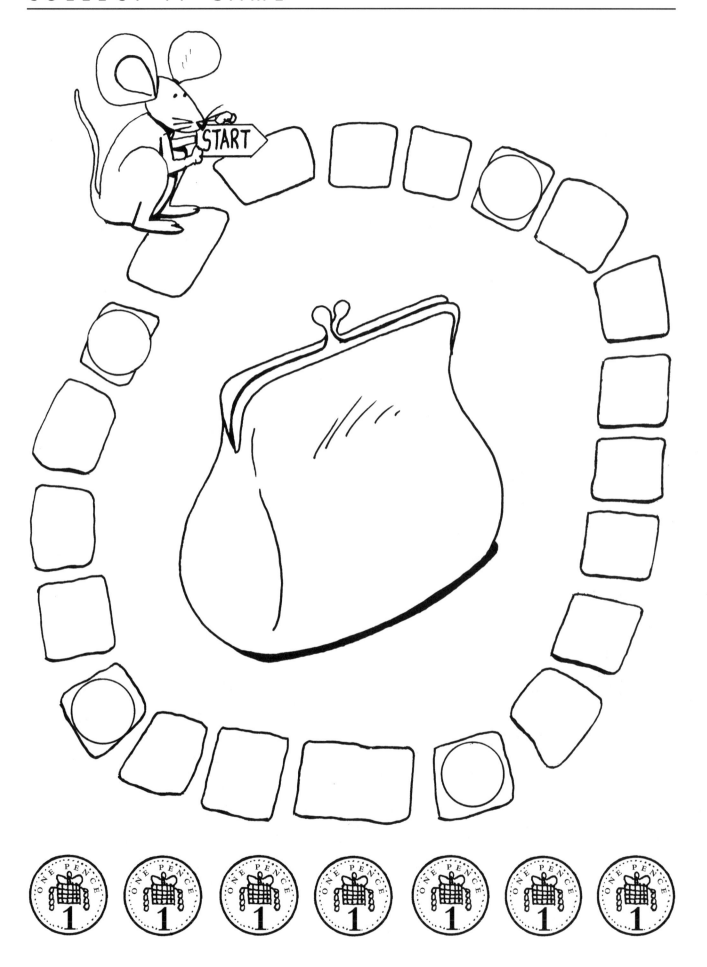

COIN TRACK GAME